ORIGINAL WRITING

from

IRELAND'S OWN

2012

ORIGINAL WRITING

ISBNS
PARENT: 978-1-78237-025-3
EPUB: 978-1-78237-026-0
MOBI: 978-1-78237-027-7
PDF: 978-1-78237-028-4

A CIP catalogue for this book is available from the National Library.

Published by ORIGINAL WRITING LTD., Dublin, 2012

Printed by CLONDALKIN GROUP, Dublin 17.

INTRODUCTION

Ireland's Own, in conjunction with Original Writing, is delighted to bring to readers this third Anthology of the winners and other highly commended entries in our annual writing competitions. The success of our first two collections, which were very well received, has encouraged us to publish our third book which we feel confident will once again be thoroughly enjoyed.

Apart from our regular corps of professional and part-time contributors, Ireland's Own receives a great many unsolicited submissions every week, many of them of a very good standard. Writing has never been so popular and we do try to be sympathetic and encouraging in our approach. We are only able to use a small portion of these but we are constantly reminded of the great hunger there is out there among people who desire to express themselves and commit their ideas to print.

We have been running our Annual Short Stories and Memories Writing Competitions for many years, and they attract a very high-standard response. For the past five years we have been supported in this by the self-publishing company, Original Writing, from Dublin, and their backing is greatly appreciated and our partnership with them has again made this anthology possible.

We congratulate the prizewinners and all the other writers included. We thank them all for their help and co-operation with this project and hope they are justifiably proud of the end result. We also compliment the hundreds of others who entered the competitions.

We specially thank bestselling author Patricia Scanlan for providing us with a foreword for the book; her support and encouragement is greatly appreciated and we feel sure her words will be taken to heart by our writers, and by all those who are bitten by the writing bug.

We thank former Ireland's Own editors, Gerry Breen and Margaret Galvin, for all their help with the annual competitions. A special word of thanks to Martin Delany, Garrett Bonner, Steven Weekes and all the crew at Original Writing for their expertise and assistance.

We meet a few old friends in this third collection, but there are a few others who are being published in a book for the first time and it is very special for them in particular. Inclusion in this anthology is a significant step for all the writers involved; we wish them all future success if they pursue their writing ambitions. Ireland's Own is happy to have played a part in helping you along the way.

Phil Murphy, Monthly Editor
Sean Nolan, Weekly Editor
Ireland's Own.

FOREWORD

by Patricia Scanlan
International Bestselling Author

I am honoured to have been invited by Ireland's Own to write a Foreword to this new anthology of short stories and memory pieces.

I would like to congratulate all the writers who have had their work selected for this prestigious book and I commend Ireland's Own for their continued support and commitment to new Irish writers.

Telling stories is in our lifeblood. The tradition of the seanchaí is ingrained in us and it is why we have so many wonderful writers in every genre.

It is a very special moment to see your work in print. All the hours spent thinking, writing, editing, rewriting, polishing the last draft until you can do no more, are worth every second for that unique feeling of achievement when you see your words on the page.

I would encourage each and every one of you to keep writing, whether it's with a view to being published, or just for your own private pleasure and entertainment. Let the words flow, let the stories flow. Hold on to your dreams and make them a reality.

Write the way that suits you. Write your own story and not a mere pale imitation of some author whose success you aspire to emulate. Be true to yourself and your characters. Feel them, believe in them, make them as real for your reader as they are for you.

But most of all ENJOY your writing. There is no better advice I can give you than that. Enjoy! Enjoy! Enjoy!

Once again, to all the writers who have succeeded in getting published in this terrific anthology, congratulations. And if you missed out this year...there's always next year's one to try again.

Happy writing and warmest wishes.

Patricia Scanlan

ORIGINAL WRITING

Original Writing Limited ('OW') has had an association with Ireland's Own for a number of years both as sponsor of the magazine's writing competitions and as publisher of the 'Original Writing From Ireland's Own' Over these years there have been many wonderful entries and it was with this in mind that we came up with the idea for the anthology. We would like to take this opportunity to congratulate all of the winners and other authors whose writings are contained in this anthology.

Original Writing Limited is a member of the Original Writing Group of companies which offers outlets for the written word across a number of websites devoted to publishing and creative writing. One of the products offered may be of particular interest to readers of Ireland's Own who also write in their spare time or have family members or friends who write.

OW can now give the writer an opportunity to have his or her work collected in one place and a paperback of bookshop quality with four colour cover, produced by OW to distribute to family, friends and colleagues. Page counts can be as low as twelve and orders are accepted from five copies. Prices start at €2.65 per copy.

We also run Writing4all which is an online writers' resource where you can share your creative writing - from poetry to short stories and from memoirs to novels - get feedback and comment on other writers' work. There is also news, events, competition information and listings for creative writing courses, writing groups, workshops and many more writing resources. Check out the site at: **www.writing4all.ie**

Contact Original Writing Limited at **01-6174834** or **info@5to50books.ie**. Further details are also available at **www.5to50books.ie** or **www.originalwriting.ie**

CONTENTS

COMPETITION WINNERS

From Pigtails To Pony Tails

^{BY} Mary Gallagher
Ballisodare, Co. Sligo

A girl attends boarding school, her first time away from home. She adjusts to her new life but then has to cope with her first tragedy

M y family make their way out through the gate towards the blue Volkswagen Beetle. I make my way toward the dining room and walk into a future where everyone and everything is strange. It is September 1958, the leaves are beginning to fall and summer slips into autumn. Light is fading. The seeds of a new beginning are in train as I walk with the head girl towards the dining room. The refectory is alive with the boisterous energy of around one hundred teenagers.

The clatter of some one hundred cups saucers, plates and cutlery fills the air. Tea is served in giant grey teapots, milk already poured inside. There is hilarity in the exchanges and everybody seems to know everybody else. I am seated beside another first year and as I say my name, I want to run away to a place where I am already known by name. The senior girls hover around serving food and making jokes I don't understand.

If only I could get to the dormitory and unpack my belongings, I might begin to feel connected to myself again. I catch a glimpse of myself in the glass of the Sacred Heart picture and a stranger looks back, dressed in clothes that seem too big, too long and too dark. As I look down at my feet I see my black lyle stockings and sensible black, thick soled shoes. A bell signals the end of supper and I make my way with two new girls to the dormitory.

Sr. Berchmans recites the rosary walking up and down the corridor. We respond in the midst of preparing for bed. The recitation feels safe and familiar and links me with home. As I fall asleep on my first night in Boarding School I wonder are they missing me at home, are they wondering how I am or have they already forgotten about me.

I awaken to the call of the bell at ten to seven in the morning, wash and dress hastily and make my way with the rest of the students to the study hall. I open a book and endeavour to study taking my cue from the older pupils who seem absorbed in their studies. I need more sleep.

At twenty five past seven we march to the Boarders' Chapel and while we wait for Mass, we pray, we dream, we remember, we forget, we giggle, and we worship or sleep. We march to the dining room, finish breakfast and walk back to the study hall. After nine o clock we make our way to the classrooms, our books in order until lunchtime.

Class succeeds class until lessons are over. Tea-time, walk time, games time, study time, leisure time, bed time, fill each day and our lives revolve around these activities. They seem set in stone and gradually we become people of habit, of order.

My family see secondary education as a wonderful opportunity for opening new doors into the future and I enjoy the many new vistas offered for enlargement. Not many students are able to avail of Secondary School education unless they are near enough to walk or cycle to a local school, or go to boarding school. Location decides educational destiny. I feel privileged to have this chance.

I open my arms and my mind to embrace this gift but I do not know about partings and the feelings engendered by these events. I look forward to the holidays and to home and on the eve of our departure we play high jinks in the dormitory. We feel the disappointment of the sister-in-charge at our behaviour. It was as if the thought of imminent freedom became too much for us to contain ourselves any longer. There is no time for punishment for at lunchtime next day we are departing.

At Christmas home feels different. My mother is now in hospital in Dublin, the house is strange without her, and is to become stranger still, a foreshadowing of what is to come. I sense life has gone on without me. The rooms seem smaller, the ceilings lower, the pots and pans tinier and I no longer fit fully in either world.

The freedom of the countryside is breathtaking, the open fields, the woods and waters, the tall trees and low stone walls all open out before me, restoring my well being. Closed doors and locked gates begin to recede, rules and regulations are forgotten. I am pampered with good wholesome food and plenty of sleep and a little work.

The neighbours remark on how well I must be doing as I grow into a tall slim strapping girl. I don't like these remarks. As the days flow into weeks, leaving home again looms menacingly in front of me and the thought of meeting my new friends sets a song in my heart.

Arriving at the gates this time, I take my bag heavily laden with goodies to supplement the plain boarding school food, to soften a hard place. It's time to say goodbye again, tears are quickly wiped away. My family set off for home in the blue Volkswagen Beetle. I search for my friends as I walk into an ordered world that separates the secular and the sacred, work and worship, study and leisure.

The humdrum of everyday is periodically broken when nuns' feastdays are celebrated. Food is plentiful and attractive, music and films are included. The hall resonates with song and dance and life is so good again that loneliness for home is temporarily obliterated.

I remember moments in a dimly lit chapel, quiet silence, a skirt rustling, a rosary beads rattling, a sigh, a smile, a prayer, a request, a wish, a leaf blowing in the wind as the door opens or shuts. We are surrounded by stained glass windows of saints and scholars, light penetrating through the changing weather of sun, cloud and rain, reality outside, hope inside.

Fervour flows all around, beauty in the red carnations and white chrysanthemums. Rich aromas mingle with Benediction incense and waft across the altar rail and are suspended in the space between the nuns' choir and boarders' chapel cut off by an altar rail. A side view of the Great Presence holds together our joys and sorrows, our hopes and disappointments.

A sense of mystery, of sacredness pervades our being in odd moments and we rest in its sustenance until it is time to go back to field and farm, to city street and small town businesses and return to the womb of home for another few weeks.

And the end of first year comes, July 1959, a warm hot summer. Nature is at its ripest, hedges laden with growth, trees shining at their fullest and yet containing the seeds of autumn, the turning of the year, the fading of summer.

With this stage backdrop comes my mother's death on a warm, bright July morning. I remember the whispers at the end of the stairs for weeks beforehand. The nurse, doctor and priest call regularly and yet I miss the meaning of these visits. I understand that my mother's cancer is serious but I do not want to know it is terminal. None of the four of us children want to believe that life can be so cruel.

It is hard to learn so early in life that we do not control destiny, sometimes destiny robs us of what we think we have a right to and we are powerless before its stealth. It is a lost summer. It is September again and this time it's my father who takes me back to boarding school in the blue Volkswagen Beetle. He carries my bag into the yard and makes a quick exit before the nuns offer their sympathy and he feels unable to take their kind offerings. He does not want to cry in public.

Over the next few weeks the students stare strangely at me or divert their eyes. I hear their whispers, "her mother is dead". They are not unkind, they just do not know what to say and neither do I. I don't want to talk about it because if I did, I would collapse with grief. There are moments and private space in the quietness of the chapel where I can be with my thoughts and feelings without being noticed or disturbed.

When I go home at Hallowe'en I wonder have I made this tragedy up, perhaps she will be there ... it is only wishful thinking. The core is gone from home, its heart is not beating anymore. My sister tries to keep home running as it used to be. My father and brothers try to be brave as they do the chores on the farm. The two girls take care of inside the house. My father teaches me how to drive.

At Christmas I arrive home with a beautiful homemade Christmas cake fully iced and decorated, won in a raffle. My mother must have arranged this, my child voice says, maybe she will do more good things for us, my wishing voice says.

My Dad's single sister Frances visits often and brings much sunshine into our lives with her compassion, security and generosity. She is there as an anchor, a sounding board, a style expert, a smart shopper, a connoisseur of beauty in food and scenery. Her presence redresses the balance somewhat and we acclimatise ourselves to the new shape we are being pressed into.

Different pieces of literature speak to my present experience. Peig Sayers endures a difficult life; the Lady of Shalott suffers unrequited love; Robert Herrick grieves that his daffodils haste away so soon. Subliminally I am touched by such thoughts and they help me to find firmer ground under my shaky feet.

Cathriona, Anne and Maureen become my steadfast friends. We talk, we dream, we share our imagined future, chiefly of falling in love, meeting the perfect husband and living happily ever after. There is also the ideal of following the religious life, constantly idealised as the best way forward. We see former pupils entering the convent and are in awe at their calling. We exchange letters during the holidays and we look forward eagerly to meeting again.

Already the loneliness, the absence from home is becoming normal. The gates are still locked, the rules still in place; it's the way things are and change happens slowly. Leaving home each time becomes a little easier because the routine is in place and the intensity of loneliness is of shorter duration. I know I am able to tolerate these absences.

I am familiar with the way things work in this system and now my greatest concern is being prepared for our biggest examination, the Leaving Certificate. There are no great points to be achieved, just pass or honours. The final day arrives, farewells are said, promises are made of meeting soon again and exchanging letters.

Suddenly it seems this is not such a prison after all. The big world is looming ahead and I have no idea yet where I am going. Five years have passed; five summers, with the length of five long winters! New gates are opening before me, old gates are about to close behind me and once again I walk into an uncertain future.

I am now on the cusp of womanhood. I leave behind the ways of the child and with the courage and brashness of youth I know things will work out somehow, someway. Once again my father arrives in the blue Volkswagen Beetle, to transport me back for the summer to the farm and the fields, the woods and the waters.

THE OLD FOX FUR STOLE

BY HELEN CORLEY
Athlone, Co. Westmeath

*Great Aunt Bea's weekly visits become a
Sunday ritual to be endured by all
the family*

Last week as I was walking through an antique shop I came across a stuffed fox in a glass case. I was immediately catapulted back in time to my childhood in the fifties and to the visits of my great-aunt Bea who graced us with her presence every Sunday.

The ritual started after supper every Saturday night. My three sisters and I squirmed and protested as our normally straight hair was tortured and twisted around strips of cloth that would, hopefully, produce rows of ringlets on Sunday morning. The shoes were polished and left on a sheet of newspaper at the side of the fire and our Sunday clothes draped on the line that stretched across the kitchen.

By twelve o'clock noon on Sunday the kitchen was like a furnace, the roast or chicken sizzling away in the range and the potatoes and veg simmering on top of it.

My mother swept damp tendrils of hair off her hot forehead while we set the table and covered the milk jug with a little circle of lace edged with tiny beads.

The cat was evicted from her cushion on the fireside chair and the cushion taken outside and shaken vigorously, lest, Heaven forbid, a stray hair might attach itself to aunt Bea's cardigan, which was a relic of the time she was housekeeper to a titled family.

Throughout all this frenzy of activity my father sat calmly in the porch reading the paper. Every other Sunday my mother would say, 'I'm not going to be entertaining this one for the rest of her life, looking down her nose at us with her delusions of grandeur'.

On the dot of one o'clock, she'd arrive in her gleaming Morris Minor and wait lady-like for my father to open the door and help her out. The rest of us would stand at the door with smiles pasted onto our faces. She would hand her brass-topped walking stick to one of us, fan herself with her gloves before slipping off her long fawn coat and the fox fur, complete with eyes, paws and tail , which she wore slung loosely over her shoulders. I hated handling that poor dead fox.

Seated at the head of the table, she imperiously informed my mother that she would have just a half bowl of soup. She reprimanded us for gulping our soup, informing us that soup was eaten from the side of the spoon.

The meat was always a bit overdone; if we had chicken, it was stringy and tough and really we children should be properly educated with regards to table manners.

My mother's face flushed, her lips tightened, but she was of the old school who would never commit the offence of insulting someone in her own home. Most Sundays we had apple pie and custard, she always found the tart slightly sour and if we had semolina pudding she found it a bit dry.

She would spend the afternoon sitting by the fireside in the only good chair and regale my mother with stories of her years in the big house. She liked tea and scones at four o'clock and she made it quite clear that she was used to china cups. She left on the dot of seven and the entire procedure was reversed, walking stick, coat, hat and the fur of that poor fox was draped over her shoulders. We would stand at the gate and wave until she rounded the corner. My mother would glare at my father and say, 'Very gracious of her to visit the peasants, just for once I'd like a Sunday to myself'.

Out of the blue came the message that Aunt Bea had fallen and broken her hip. She was in the County hospital. We visited her every day and listened to her complaints about the doctors and nurses. At eighty years of age, it was unlikely that she would ever be able to live alone again. How she would hate life in a "Home".

One evening the matron was speaking to mammy. Jokingly she said, 'Of course we could never hope to compare with a paragon like you, we hear all about your great cooking skills and meticulous housekeeping, not to mention your mannerly children who are all geniuses. Her visits to you were the highlight of her life. She even threatens to tell you if she feels we are a bit slow to attend to her'.

That evening we cleared out the front room, lit a fire in the small grate, set up a bed beside the window, collected Bea and settled her in there where she stayed until her death at the age of ninety. Her good clothes, including the poor dead fox, were stored in a trunk that reeked of camphor.

TRAGEDY IN KILMUCKLA

By DENIS O'NEILL
Rochfortbridge, Co. Westmeath

The locals gather in the local village pub after the funeral to discuss the tragedy of Dick Clancy and its implications

A dozen or so customers sat almost motionless at the bar of Ryan's pub as the wag on the wall clock chimed ten o'clock. Ryan's was the only pub in the small farming community of Kilmuckla. It was a country pub on the border of Tipperary and Offaly where the dress code was 'come as you are', Wellington boots were more often than not the footwear of choice for the mainly male customers and the Massey Ferguson 135 was the most popular vehicle in the car park.

Kilmuckla was more of a gathering of houses at a crossroads than a village. The parish church with the small parochial house in the grounds, the national school and Johnny Ryan's pub were the main buildings. A few simple houses lined the narrow street. The crossroads was the place to win or lose your last few shillings playing pitch and toss.

Ryan's pub was the nearest shop, the local post office, the unofficial community centre and the hub of the community. It was a place where you could get a half pound of ham, a bag of calf nuts and a pint of porter at eleven o'clock at night, and all three served over the same counter. Johnny himself had a small farm and always presented himself well enough to serve his punters. Though his main income was the pub, he was often seen serving behind the bar with a pair of Wellington boots on.

Earlier that day the entire population of the parish of Kilmuckla and beyond had turned out en masse, despite the wintry December weather, to offer their sympathies to the Clancy family and attend the funeral of Dick Clancy. Such a tragic event drew what was possibly the biggest funeral cortege in the area since Father O'Farrell was buried on Christmas Eve, nineteen fifty nine, almost ten years ago to the day.

All the mourners and neighbours had gathered in Ryan's pub after the funeral to thaw out with a hot whiskey or just to swallow the lump in their throat with a pint of porter. It was a ritual as well revered as the burial itself to gather in the local pub afterwards.

As the evening passed slowly, one by one the mourners parted company and by ten o'clock most had gone home, all but the dozen or so regulars remained and tried hard to get the conversation back to normality. Breaking the silence, the outside door was whipped open, almost blew off its hinges with the force of the cold east wind as in stormed Dinny Maher. Bowing his head to avoid hitting the lintel, Dinny, or "Long Dinny" as he was affectionately known, he being six foot six in his stocking feet, took just two paces from the door to reach the bar.

'A pint Jimmy' he said in an almost whisper as he pulled up a bar stool and exchanged the usual weather related greetings to all.

'Shocking night' was his opening entry into the general conversation.

'Shocking sad funeral that' he continued, not directing his comment to anyone in particular but open to whomever was first to reply.

'Shocking to the world' said Jimmy Ryan, filling Long Dinny's pint of stout, 'shocking to see a young man killed like that... with a young wife and child... in the mouth of Christmas'.

Jimmy placed the pint of porter in front on Dinny. 'That's on the house Dinny' he said in a mournful tone. Jimmy was a noble man and his gesture was a mark of respect for the dead.

'Poor Maura was in an awful state' added Tommy Daly, as he shifted his gaze from the Farmers Journal to engage in the conversation. He folded his newspaper and placed it on the counter and with an emotional intake of breath said 'Her little gossoon didn't know what was going on'

'Ah sure that poor child will never remember his father' said Long Dinny, 'sure the lad won't be four years of age until next spring'.

The entire congregation at the bar opened into the same conversation. What happened? How was Dick Clancy killed? Everyone who made a contribution had a little more to add and a full picture of the events leading up to the tragic death of Dick began to unfold.

Old Andy Gavin had the full story and took to the floor. When old Andy spoke, everyone listened. Andy was the 'village elder' so to speak and was consulted on all matters. Andy, now in his seventies, famed for his heroic actions, shoulder to shoulder with the Irish martyrs of the 1916 Rising as a young lad of sixteen, was a very well respected member of the community.

'I'll tell ye all what happened' said Andy, tipping back his cap as he wiped the porter from his mouth with a less than sparkling white hanky. 'He went out to feed the few cattle he has at the back of Lahy's Bog'. Andy had the full attention of all in the pub.

'His tractor got stuck in the wet ground and he got out to peg out the few bales of hay to the cattle... that big red bull of his hit him straight in the chest with a puck and knocked the wind clean out of him... Dick fell over with the bale of hay on top of him'.

Andy paused, taking a big gulp out of his pint; he wiped his mouth once again and continued... 'Sure with the cattle wound up to get a fresh bit of hay.... wasn't poor Dick trampled into the ground... he never had a chance...God rest his soul'.

The entire place fell silent. Andy pulled back his bar stool and sat down again holding his half empty pint with both of his hands.

'Jesus, he must have got an awful death' said Jimmy as he rested both elbows on the counter 'and poor auld Eamon Mullen found him'.

'Eamon found him,' replied Andy, looking forlornly into his pint 'almost totally buried in the mud... he heard the tractor still ticking over... Eamon told me yesterday morning that Dick was killed instantly... trampled into the ground.'

'What time of the day was it?' asked Noel Breen, an old friend and neighbour of Clancy's. 'I thought I heard a tractor in Lahy's Bog the other evening around eight o'clock or so,' he confessed. 'Jesus, if I had only went down there...' Noel paused and almost took the blame for the tragedy

'Sure he was killed outright' said Andy.

'I heard Dick's tractor pass the house at twenty five minutes to eight' he continued his tale as he gathered himself again and took his pipe out of his pocket for a smoke.

'Maura got afraid when he wasn't home by nine to get the news upon the wireless'.

Andy was accurate and had the full account in detail. Andy didn't add or subtract, as was often the case in an event of such magnitude in rural Ireland.

'Eamon Mullen had just finished the milking and was heading home,' continued Andy, speaking through the side of his mouth as he lit his pipe. 'And Maura asked him to see if he had broken down or got a puncture or something'.

Eamon Mullen was the farm hand at Clancy's farm, a hard worker and time of day or weather conditions didn't affect him one iota. If there was a job to de done, winter or summer, midnight or midday, Eamon was always there.

Eamon left school after sixth class; he never knew anything only farming. He began his work as a gossoon with Old Dick Clancy, Dick's father. Old Dick thought the world of him and when he died, Dick kept him on as a farm hand and friend. Eamon was part of the furniture in Clancy's house and would walk in and put on the kettle himself for tea if there was no one at home.

Eamon was very much trusted and a family friend of the Clancys, well respected and liked in the entire community.

Eamon, not the worst looking man in the town by a long way, lived alone in the small cottage that he was born in on the outskirts of the village. Both his parents were dead and with only one sister who was now married and living near Thurles, Eamon's life was Clancy's farm.

Eamon, a fit young man in his thirty's was an eligible bachelor, though he was not in the market for a wife or even a steady girlfriend. He was happy to live alone. Eamon was hurt badly when his childhood sweetheart broke his heart and hence, love or romance was not his top priority.

He'd had a soft spot for young Mandy O'Reilly years ago. Everyone in the village thought that there would be wedding bells ringing for Eamon and Mandy but Mandy packed her bags at age seventeen and left Eamon and Kilmuckla high and dry. She went off to seek her fortune in Australia, leaving without even a goodbye, and never looked back.

Eamon never got over Mandy and didn't look the side of another woman from the day she left. The locals knew that Eamon was holding out to see if Mandy would ever return.

All this and more was discussed over drinks in Ryan's pub until limber tongued with a belly full of beer, Johnny Delaney, the local hard fellow and known for being a bit of a nuisance with drink in him, announced what everyone had been thinking but with respect for the newly widowed Maura Clancy, they daren't say. Only Johnny Delaney could have the lack of decorum to speak so out of place.

'Eamon Mullen will fall in for that farm,' said Johnny as he downed the last of his pint. 'Mark my words' he said with a definite tone of argument if anyone wanted to take up the debate.

'You have enough now Johnny.' said Jimmy Ryan sternly. 'Dick Clancy isn't cold in his grave and you have Maura signing the farm over to Eamon'.

'Mark my words,' insisted Johnny... 'Eamon Mullen runs that farm...sure what does Maura Clancy know about farming'... he persisted, looking for anyone to take up the argument, but no one would entertain him.

'Time for you to go home now Johnny,' said Jimmy, 'And leave that car where it is' he said as he looked up at the clock and called time.

'Time now lads, it's been a long day,' he shouted as he leaned over to one of his most trusted customers, Tom Daly.

'Will you leave Johnny Delaney home?' he asked. 'He has been here since after the funeral'.

Tom Daly bundled Johnny Delaney into his car and they were the last to leave the pub.

The shutters were closed on what was a solemn day as Jimmy tidied up the pub. After washing the few glasses and giving the counter a good wipe from one end to the other, Jimmy took a whiskey glass and filled himself a half one. Taking a little sip from his drink Jimmy then rearranged the barstools and gave the floor a quick sweep, emptied the ash trays and sat on a barstool at the end of the counter.

He took off his cap and bowed his head, blessing himself with a wave of his hand more so than a sign off the cross, Jimmy began the Memorare for the repose of the soul of Dick Clancy. Mid way through his prayer Jimmy put back on his cap and stood up. Looking up to the ceiling he downed the last of his whiskey and spoke aloud.

'Is there any justice up there at all' he said... 'Taking away a fine man Like Dick Clancy... in his prime, with a young wife and child... and leaving that lay-about Johnny Delaney here to annoy me'.

THE DISTANT HEART

BY MARTIN MALONE
Athy, Co. Kildare

Elderly Jimmy is determined to overcome his fear of flying to keep a promise to his emigrant son in America

'You're sure that you'll be up to the journey?' Eileen said, his new carer, one who hardly knew him. They were in the kitchen in his mid-terrace home. A small stove burned logs to take the chill from the morning air. Sad curtains, confederate grey, she pulled back to allow in daylight.

'Yes, ah...I've never been there, you know,' he said.

'Really?' she said, picking his walking stick off the lino, 'and why not?'

He reflected on this for moments. He had once been a well-built man, a carpenter, regarded as a horse of a man, a county footballer, but now his flesh sat closely to his bones and the collapse seemed to thicken out the wrinkles; his bones resembled tent poles propping up a sagging canvas.

He said quietly, 'I've never been out of the country.'

'Ever?' Eileen asked.

He shook his head.

'Not even to the States when...'

'Never.'

He thought Eileen was a gas woman. Heavyset and not a clock-watcher, unlike some of his other former carers, they seemed always anxious to be done with him.

'And what was the reason behind that?' Eileen said.

'I could never bear the thoughts of going into a tube and taking to the sky – the very notion made me feel quite ill.'

'And has that fear left you?' He shook his head and said, 'This is something I should have gotten over years ago, Eileen – wasn't

I the awful coward? Do you know I went up to the steps of the airplane with poor Ivy, that time to see Michael in Boston, and told her I couldn't go...just couldn't.'

'You left her there?'

'I did.'

'On the steps?'

'On the steps.'

'She must have been terribly hurt.'

'No – she saw the sweat on my face, the ashen colour, and knew...ah Ivy was the sort who didn't know how to hold a bad feeling towards someone. God be kind to her.'

'I see. Why do you want to bother with flying now, at your age, Jimmy – putting hardship on yourself?'

'I made a promise to Michael to go see him before I die.'

Eileen went to speak but remembered that Jimmy had had a medical appointment with his doctor and that he had said it hadn't gone well, not adding anything further.

'We had a falling out,' he said, 'years ago. The row was over nothing really.'

'When we look back at them, they usually are, Jimmy.'

'But we made up – we used to ring each other you know and I said I was sorry and he was like his mother, a good heart, luckily for me.'

She gathered that Jimmy had been a man who thought that saying 'sorry' was a sign of weakness and apologies hardly ever leaked from him.

He sighed, 'You see, I got fierce vexed with him when he told me that he had taken out American citizenship. I thought it a betrayal of his homeland – how can a man swear allegiance to another country and yet still claim to be Irish through and through... to me it was an act of high treason.'

Silence.

'I still think that it is, Eileen. Men on my side of the family died in the fight for Irish freedom – they died so Irishmen could have an Irish passport – do you follow me? '

'It's sad that you think that way – I have a daughter there who did the same – America gave her the opportunity that her home country didn't.It never caused me to lose any sleep.'

'He wanted to become a cop – that was his reason – I let it go and stopped making an issue out of it. I had to. I had lost him to the States because of the inadequacies of this sorry country of ours but I didn't want to lose him entirely. But I always had the sup of bitterness about it in me. Two passports, two hearts – hearts that'd turn in a heartbeat...the old Irish failing, eh, that of the traitor – it comes natural to some, I suppose.'

'You're an old fool, Jimmy O'Leary, to be thinking like that – it's that sort of mindset that's ruined this country.'

'I'm a patriot.'

'Are you now? Indeed. Well, my Mary's a patriot too – she loves Ireland, and she loves her new home in Chicago and her children love coming over to see me – your son like my daughter didn't leave Ireland for no reason – they were forced out. Patriotism my behind, Jimmy – I'd have lost the run of myself if I'd been married to you, the run of myself, entirely. I would have been a danger to you.'

He looked at her and then at the clock – she was over her time. She was right, of course, Michael had had to leave Ireland to find work, to create a life for himself. Strange that he ended up being a detective in Boston – he'd applied for the guards here but was turned down because he had failed Irish in his Leaving Certificate. Aye, Irish. And not more than two people spoke it in the town – kept to the classroom mainly. The country pushed many good people out to the margins.

'Hmm,' he said, 'have you time for tea – and would you open that carton of milk for me?'

'And shure you've probably got no passport, have you, Jimmy?'

There's a thing. He hadn't.

'I thought so – well, if you're going to America you better get yourself one.'

She got up and put on the kettle. 'Will you give me a hand to book the flight and all – I wouldn't know where to start.' She knew his reading and writing skills were poor. He'd left school at fourteen and had admitted to her that he had never finished reading a book – the sports pages did for him.

'Passport is where you start, Jimmy.'

'Okay.'

'I'll get you the form.'

'Good woman.'

'Don't you patronise me – two hearts indeed. Once they're both good does it matter?'

'I suppose not.'

Over the following weeks his plans began to take shape: Eileen helped him to fill out the passport application, he changed some of his savings into dollars, booked his flight – he argued a little with her when she requested wheelchair assistance for him, helped him to pick out some gifts for Michael's family.

At night the terrors of flying came to him and he would lie awake thinking about being in the air, shifting his thoughts back and forth to the positive things Eileen had told him to dwell upon; flying was one of the safest modes of travelling, it would be like sitting at home in his armchair; he would have a mini-TV in front of him with a choice of movies and radio channels; he would have dinner, it would all be over before he knew it.

She did not understand, however, it was the 'boxed in' feeling that he dreaded. A car was different – it was easy to pull over and get out. But when you're 3000 feet in the air, that's a different story. When he told her this on a Monday morning Eileen laughed and said, 'You'll be up way over 30,000 feet, not 3,000 – Jimmy...you're a scream.'

'30, 000,' he whispered.

'Put that on your carpenter's measuring tape and smoke it.'

Friday evenings he met with some of his old friends in the snug at The Vatican. It was a crew that time was thinning slowly but surely. They played darts, cards and talked openly about personal issues concerning each other's health, the treatment, the non-treatment, the sport, always sport, usually about football, hurling and soccer and rugby, horse-racing. But every topic led back to their health.

'Suck on a sweet, Jimmy, when you're taking off, 'one said.

'Why?'

'It'll stop your ears popping.'

'I see.'

'Your ears pop when you reach altitude – you get a ringing noise in your ears, maybe an earache, but that doesn't happen too often.'

'I have a ringing in my ears already,' Jimmy said.

'And if you look out the window and see an engine on fire, call one of the cabin crew.'

Silence.

'What'll she do?' Jimmy asked.

'I dunno – but she'll probably never have seen one on fire before.'

Someone else said, 'That's lame – I heard a joke like that on the Late Late – don't be worrying about flying Jimmy, you'll be grand. And if anything does happen – remember this: you're 77 and had a good life, and it'll be over quickly.'

Hah, hah, a tiny eruption of laughter, and then an order for a round of drinks.

Michael's dropping of the 'O' from the family name had also rankled Jimmy. They were O'Learys not Learys. Why did Michael decide to do that? Was there a practical reason? He supposed he would never find out now: when he had resolved his quarrel with Michael he had determined to cover no old ground with him. Moving on meant not raking over old coals.

Eileen insisted on driving him to the airport.

'Isn't terminal an awful word to describe those buildings,' he said, as they entered the car park at Terminal 2.

She thought about it and then said on a laugh, 'Jimmy, aren't you the morbid man.'

He had yet to spoil part of her plan and didn't announce it until after he had checked in. 'Jimmy,' she said, 'the wheelchair will make life much easier for you – you won't have to wait in line, you'll be first on to the plane and...'

She let her words trail to nothingness because she saw that she was wasting her time trying to reason with him.

'Look Eileen I can walk fine with me old cane and sometimes I don't even need it to get by – but I'd sooner crawl into the plane on my belly than get in a wheelchair – now don't get me wrong, If I needed one, I'd use it, but I'd have to really, really need one – do you understand me?'

'I used to think my father was the most stubborn man I would ever have had the misfortune to meet, but I was wrong.'

'Now,' he said, 'come and have breakfast with me – a terminal breakfast.'

At the door to the plane he baulked. Then a hostess smiled at him, looked at his ticket and directed him to his seat in First Class. He was next to a window and looked out for a few minutes at the ground, the pelting rain, and then at the other passengers filing past. People of all ages – men and women older than him, babies, youngsters who he thought looked to be seasoned fliers.

'This'll be a piece of cake,' he told himself.

The woman who sat in beside him wasn't one for talking. He'd said, 'Hello' and introduced himself and she half-smiled at him and was polite, but he knew she wouldn't want an old guy talking to her throughout the flight.

Take-off. He looked at the earth falling away and was braced for something bad to happen. He sucked hard on a clove drop, felt his ears go whoosh. Whenever there was even the slightest of turbulence he searched for traces of trepidation on the faces of the cabin crew and the other passengers. He put on a headset and had the woman next to him show him how to operate the TV – he watched a film and slept through dinner, through the flight, till it was almost time to land.

'You snore,' the woman said next to him on landing, not kindly.

Well, that was one hard bit behind him – the hardest part had yet to come: to meet with Michael's family, to get in their people carrier for the short drive to the cemetery to see his son's grave and say his goodbyes in person, to keep his promise to his son that he would visit him one day; to prove that never again would he allow a long distance to grow between their hearts.

A Teller Of Tales

By Sean O'Doherty
Raheny, Dublin

The arrival of the travelling storyteller was a harbinger of Summer and a break from the usual classes in the late 1940s.

We never knew his real name. He was known locally as Seamus the Seanachaí – a spinner of stories, a teller of tales. He was a small stocky man dressed in rough tweeds, faded corduroy trousers and hob nailed boots. He boasted a fáinne on his left lapel and a red spotted kerchief com cravat protected his scrawny neck from the harsh winds of winter.

His arrival in our village was the harbinger of summer and the lengthening of the days. It usually coincided with our age old custom of placing the May boughs on the doors steps in the village. Ours was a generation that had yet to experience modern high-tech achievements. T.Vs and videos were unknown, while PCs, mobiles and consoles were at this time - the late forties – as far distant as Neil Armstrong and the walk on the moon.

Our entertainment was largely home grown, cost little or nothing at all, and was as active as our imaginations.

The advent of the Seanachaí meant a complete break from class. An tAthair Peadar's 'Mo Scéal Fein' (My Own Story) was put aside and the Irregular Verbs were left to mystify us for another day. The Master's ancient wheelie board was trundled aside and a small clearance made in front of the flagged fireplace.

Even though May had arrived the Master liked a small turf fire in the grate, mainly to boil his kettle. We loved the smell of the peat as the smoke drifted up the chimney.

Our storyteller was a Mystery Man. Nobody knew from whence he came, or where he went, or more intriguing, where he wintered in the 'off season'. We accepted the fact that as Spring followed Winter so came our terpsichorean to enchant his eager audience.

All the classes had assembled in the Big Room, scrambling over forms and desks to get a good vantage point. The Seanachaí used his great booming voice most effectively, without notes of any kind and nothing resembling an autocue, he carried on regardless. His memory was phenomenal, his ability to recall, remarkable.

We sat enthralled as he recounted stories from the Fenian Cycle, Celtic Sagas, and the legends of Hercules and the Greek Heroes. He almost had us in tears as he challenged our imaginations with the great tragedy of the Children of Lir. Sometimes his voice dropped to a barely audible whisper as he paused for effect. Later he broke into song and had us swinging out the rhythm of 'Oró mo Bháidin,' and 'An bhfaca tú mo Sheamaisín' (Did you see my little Seamus). We thought for years that that song was 'An bhfaca tú mo Haymachine!'

The admission fee of six pence could be won if any pupil dared to sing. Most of us were too bashful to sing in front of the Master but Tony Kane was not shy. He clambered over the forms and stood on the temporary 'stage'. He broke into a rousing rendition of 'Beigh aonach amárch í gContae an Chláir', (There's a fair tomorrow in Co. Clare), a song that had a certain resonance for us Clare folk. Tony won his prize.

Sixpence was quite a prize in those days. One penny bought a 'Peggy's Leg', another purchased a 'Liquorice Pipe'. There was always change for 'Geary's Biscuits' or 'Cleeve's Toffee'.

'Maith a fear' (Good man), said our entertainer as he presented Tony with his prize. Meanwhile, the Master put the blackened kettle on the fire and raked up the sods. Our storyteller was treated to a scalding cup of tea. The Master proffered one of his jam sandwiches and the visitor ate with relish.

Performance over, our actor bade us 'Slan Leat' (Goodbye). We cheered warmly 'Go Neirí an bothar leat' (May the road rise with you) as he collected his few belongings into a canvas bag and stepped into the crisp sunshine. He was heading for the next village and another expectant audience.

The following year Spring rolled around again and our Seanachaí didn't appear. When he hadn't appeared by early May we began to wonder. He never did come back to regale us with his epic tales. We learned later on that he had been found dead in a barn near Kilrush. He had three sixpences in his pocket, a few scraps of writing paper and surprisingly, a well-thumbed edition of 'The Rubyiat' by Omar Khayam.

'Death due to hypothermia' was the coroner's verdict. There were three people at the burial - my father, who was a member of the Garda Siochana at the time; Fr. O'Brien, and Ned, the gravedigger.

Was our Seanachaí a descendant of the Bards or Filí (poets) of old? Did his forbearers enchant kings and chieftains with their satirical verse or pastoral poetry? We'll never know but his passing did mean a break in the great oral tradition of storytelling for us.

Beginners Short Story Runner-Up

THE WEDDING

By NORA BRENNAN
Glendine Heights, Kilkenny

John had dusted down his suit to attend a neighbour's wedding,
giving it a first airing since the death of his mother
four months earlier

A bouquet of ivory roses filled the water font at the church door. John dipped his fingers in and blessed himself. Two girls stood at the entrance handing out booklets with two gold hearts overlapping and the names Julie and Denis written in the centre.

'I'm sure we'll have a while to wait,' Martin Lanigan said to John as they walked inside.

''Tis a woman's day for God's sake', Josie Lanigan said next to him. John was looking at the booklet thinking it must have cost a lot.

Inside the church, bunches of flowers and ribbons hung on the end of each pew and the altar was adorned with white lilies. Some guests had arrived and were scattered throughout the church. Women wore feathered hats and some had shawls draped across their shoulders. John recognised a few of the parishioners sporting suits and dresses, people he rarely saw out of their winter coats. He was wearing his good suit. Bought years before, it had an airing in the four months since his mother died.

He followed the Lanigans into a seat on the right; thankful they didn't go too far up the aisle. The church was in the neighbouring parish in order to hold the large number of guests. In his own parish, men sat on the left and women on the right. He felt awkward. The altar seemed lopsided and it reminded him of being back at school and the teacher forcing him to write with his right hand when he was a 'citeog'.

'Didn't she do well for herself? God be with the days when the father hadn't two shillings to rub together.' Josie whispered to her husband.

''Tis great what a bit of education does,' replied Martin. John eyed the pews to the top left of the church and caught sight of a woman dressed in mauve. It had to be Kathleen. She was ironing the hem of a lilac skirt the week before when he called with the wedding present. A large statue of the Virgin Mary stood in front of the side aisle and candles lit up her feet.

The Murphys were sitting two pews ahead of him. The giveaway was Mary Murphy's hair. She had an extravagant streak when it came to hair colour. That day it was the colour of straw and it hung like a sheaf against the nape of her neck. The next time he'd see her at Mass, it could be the colour of a ploughed field.

Sadness edged around his thoughts. The bride's mother Kathleen was his own age. When she said she wouldn't wait for him thirty years before, he knew now she was right.

'What possessed them to have the wedding at this hour?' Martin asked leaning towards John. 'They don't think much of the farmer and the milking. Quick they forget.'

'Ah sure the cows'll manage for one evening,' John replied. 'I'll give you a hand in the morning.'

A young man in a black suit walked up the side aisle. The whispers in the church died down and Fr Walsh moved to the front of the altar. John heard a flurry of activity in the porch and when the organ burst into sound, the congregation rose and women strained to get a glimpse of the bride.

-'Did you enjoy the meal John?' the bride asked as she sat in the empty chair beside him.

'Twas lovely. I won't need a bit for the Lord knows when.'

'I haven't seen you since your mother's funeral. I'm glad you came.'

'Sure, I'd hardly know you Julie, you've changed so much. And you're looking lovely. The image of your mother.'

'Thanks, and thanks too for your generous gift.'

'Ah, 'twasn't much. Ye had a great turn out today.' There were loud sounds coming from the stage as the band tested keys and microphones.

'Will ye be living in Dublin?'

'Yeah. We have to go where the work takes us. We'll be down sure. Mam is going to find it hard on her own I know. She'd never manage the few animals if she hadn't you to give her a hand. You're a great help to her.'

'Ah indeed! I don't do much.' John fingered the handle of the cup, delighted with what he had just heard. He leaned forward eager to catch whatever else she might say about him and her mother.

'I never thought she'd cope as well as she did when Daddy died. She's happier than I've seen her in a long while. But if the worst ever came to the worst, she could come and live with us.'

'Aye.' He continued to turn the empty cup, stunned by the rawness of what she had just said. He felt a sudden desire to go straight to where Kathleen Maher sat and ask her to dance. It was unconscionable that she might be gone from the parish. He remembered the evening when his mother was in hospital; waiting in the shadows for Josie and Martin to give him a lift when there was a rap on the door.

The sight of Kathleen framed against the tangerine sky startled him. She was carrying a loaf of fresh bread. She didn't delay but said she'd call again and she did. Evenings changed because of her random visits. He came back from the fields earlier to clean out the fire grate and have a good fire going. He had almost forgotten the loneliness of the empty house when his mother was in hospital.

'I hope you'll enjoy the evening John. Maybe we'll have a dance later?'

'Surely.' The bride moved swiftly away to talk to another guest. John watched Kathleen at the top table chatting to the bridesmaids. The band played 'Waltzing Matilda' and couples stepped onto the dance floor. When the song ended, he sidled over by the edge of the room. The tempo changed, the volume increased and the singer sprang about on the stage singing 'The Hucklebuck'. People abandoned conversations and started dancing. He placed a hand on Kathleen's shoulder.

'Would you care to dance?'

'Of course, I'd love to', she said smiling. Her face was radiant and he liked the fact that it hadn't a painted look. She walked ahead of him into the crowd. 'Round and round and round we go....' There were elbows moving, women swinging and skirts twirling. Catching both hands, John and Kathleen moved to the rhythm, she twisting and twirling, he with a swiftness he thought he had long forgotten. The music changed to a slow set. Lights dimmed and the ball of light in the centre of the ceiling flashed pastel shades of lemon and peach around the room. Kathleen glowed. John drew her close.

'We'll be giving them all talk,' he said.

'Never mind, John. Isn't it well to have our health for it?' she replied.

'You look as lovely as that daughter of yours,' he said tilting back his head to look into her glowing face. Kathleen didn't answer but rested her head against his. They moved in rhythm to the sound of 'Lady in Red', he felt the fullness of her warm body and her hand like a blackbird in his own. He wanted the moment to last, to forget about neighbours as they passed on the dance floor. Whatever the future held, he was sure Kathleen would help him cope.

There was a tap on his shoulder as he walked Kathleen back to the table. It was Josie Lanigan.

'We'll be heading along in a few minutes John. Paddy doesn't like driving too late and 'twill be an early start in the morning. Thanks for a grand day Kathleen.'

'Sure there's no hurry on ye. The night is only starting,' Kathleen replied. John was speechless. He couldn't leave now, not when the night was only starting and he had Kathleen to himself. It was understood he'd go home with the Lanigans since they brought him. Looking onto the dance floor, he saw the Murphys jiving. Kathleen had seen them too. 'Sure, I'll stay a while longer and travel with the Murphys.' They'll be going by the door.'

'Between all of us, someone'll get you home', Kathleen intervened.

'Thanks all the same Josie,' John said. 'I'll be over in the morning to give a hand with the cows. Good luck.' When they left, Kathleen turned and said, 'Sure if it comes to it, you can stay the night! There's a bed in my room that'd sleep four people.' He shifted the weight on his feet. He loved her directness even if he didn't know how to handle it. The band played 'Country Roads.'

'Come on, let's have another dance' he asked. He felt the energy of a teenager pulse through his veins. Young and old were shaking about; people he was used to seeing at Mass or around the village were almost beyond recognition. Women had stripped to shimmery vests and satin dresses and everywhere he looked there was flesh. Kathleen's top was sleeveless and the neckline hinted at the fullness of her bosom.

When they returned to the table, other guests approached. Some came to thank Kathleen and talk about the day. He wanted her all to himself and when that wasn't possible, he went to the toilet. On his way out of the Gents, he caught sight of a wall of mirrors ahead of him. The face he walked towards was that of an old man. Suddenly all the years of his life were thrown back in his face. What man would betray his mother and give it to say in the parish the way he did. It wasn't right for a man tilting seventy to be carrying on as he was – out dancing all night and his mother hardly cold in the grave. He looked away and steadied himself.

Ambling towards the top table, he caught a glimpse of Kathleen who smiled from the dance floor. The Murphys were sitting next to the top table.

'Ye'll be heading off at some hour?' John said joining them.

'We will. We'll be going shortly.'

'I'll travel with ye so. Martin and Josie were in an awful hurry earlier.' The bride approached the table and Mary Murphy chatted about the lace on the sleeves of her wedding dress and how she reminded her of Princess Grace. Kathleen had gone back to her table and John saw his chance before someone else came along.

'I'll be off Kathleen. The Murphys are going shortly. You'll have a long night yet catching up with all that's here.'

'Ah that's a pity. But sure I understand.'

'Thanks. 'Twas a great day.' He bent forward and whispered in her ear, 'You're looking as lovely as Princess Grace ever did.'

'Go on with yourself,' she said tapping him on the upper back. 'I'll be around with a bit of bread in a day or two.'

WILLY'S DROWNING

By JOHN PATRICK BELL

Manorhamilton, Co. Leitrim

Growing up in Belfast in the company of older people has left the now grown man with vivid memories.

A s a small boy I remember those Sunday afternoons, quiet times, which never seemed to end and it always rained. Heavy rain that bounced off the grey pavements again and again. Sunday, an Ulster Sunday when every thing seemed to be shut, except the churches and chapels and God help us there were plenty of those.

I'd sit in the parlour looking out at the grey sky full of rain with its promises of more to come, the broken gutterings spilling their contents down the red brick to stain the walls a darker hue. A city street, no flowers or grass, all corners with few soft edges.

An empty pavement broken only by the corner lamppost, frayed bits of coloured rope the young girls had twisted around its fluted stem to make a swing. It would only come to life when the lamp lighter with his long pole opened its glass face and turned the light jet on inside its mouth. Rain and silences were unbroken, except for the rustle of a Sunday newspaper or the clink of a cup in a saucer, as my aunt and my grandmother, with seemingly unquenchable thirst, drank more cups of tea. Their soft voices were almost in whispers so that even the most banal conversation sounded secretive and important.

Endless cups of tea, wetted with the sweetest of water, mountain water from mountain rain that was piped all the way from the Mountains of Mourne. So rain had its uses but to a small boy entrapped on a Sunday afternoon it was botheration and a nuisance like the flies in a summer meadow.

When we had visitors, ladies of a comparable age, the tea leaves in the drained cups would be 'read' and my grandmother, a matriarchal figure being the oldest and the wisest and gifted with 'second sight', would start the readings.

'I can see a ship or a train' she'd say; that meant a journey was on the way, the nearer the top of the cup the sooner it would occur. Which even as a small boy I found very odd as none of them hardly ever travelled out of the street! Foretelling money - well everybody knew the tea leaf form of money, it was when the tiniest of little leaves, like freckles, stuck to the side of the cup. The more leaves, the more money, as simple as that. Only, as with the travelling bit, I can't remember any of them having or getting any money. My aunt, a stitcher of shirts and unmarried, never drank or smoked, or went anywhere except to church or 'visiting'.

She never had any money, although my grandmother, judging by the worn but still fine furniture crammed into the little house, had known better times when her husband was alive. She often talked of once having a 'Rathunas', an old word from the Irish meaning prosperity, for like their speech ennobled with words from another age, most of their talk was of times gone by.

'Do you mind the time', or 'did you remember', were often the start of a reminiscence.

I having no memory of such times, would turn to gaze out at the still falling rain and think of places to go when I grew up or when the rain stopped, which ever came first!

The parlour held a tall, very ornate china cabinet that almost touched the ceiling, full of ornaments and knick-knacks, many from distant parts of the globe. The world was far more mysterious and much bigger than it is today, or so it seemed. Although of no great value, the Indian dagger and the whale's tooth were my favourites, brought home by an uncle Willy.

Now Willy, my grandmother's son, had been a merchant seaman, and never been known to return home 'empty-handed'. It was this son Willy who lay buried in Columbo, Sri Lanka, or as it was called Ceylon, having the misfortune to fall off the ship as it lay at anchor. The shipping company implied he was drunk so no compensation was ever paid, but later returning shipmates claimed he was pushed!

It was this death, the death of a son who wandered the seas on cruise ships and tramp steamers, that I remember so well. For it gave rise to a ghostly tale, a strange tale that my grandmother would often relate when the occasion arose, and a 'wake' usually provided such a platform.

Now, at a 'wake' the deceased, at least for once in their lives the centre of attention, would be laid out in their finery, for a few poor souls the best dressed they had been in years. Some were in immaculate white shrouds, locally made but unlike the fine Ulster shirts, no claims for durability would have been considered appropriate.

In poor homes for a man to be buried in his Sunday best, a sacrifice in itself, redemption from the pawnshop was often first required. The dead were 'waked' or kept company prior to the funeral or burial from the church, the manner of which depended on the religion of the deceased.

Whether they practised a religion or not didn't seem to have much bearing on the proceedings. Everyone 'belonged' to some denomination, lapsed Catholics or 'lost' Protestants were always welcomed back into the fold, especially when they were dead!

Despite talks to the contrary 'wakes' were usually well ordered affairs with prayers for the dead and great sympathy for the bereaved. A great time for talks or 'craic' and, in keeping with the atmosphere, ghostly happenings were often paraded and aired.

As a young boy I would be taken to the local 'wakes', probably for the simple reason I couldn't be left alone. As no other relatives lived close by, there was little alternative - the concept of a baby-sitter had yet to make their acquaintance or, if it had, their acceptance.

After all, young as I was, I was one of the family and as they were obviously very fond of me, they liked to show me off. Notwithstanding that, I don't suppose it had ever occurred to them that the sight of a shrivelled body in a coffin would be upsetting for a small boy.

However, it was not all sad and mournful for comedy also took a seat. The light hearted moments, the funny happenings in their often drab lives governed by a legacy of hard work and exploited by the fear of poverty, were not forgotten.

Tears and laughter mixed easily at an Irish wake and past antics of the deceased remembered, with no offence taken and none intended. The people had to make their own amusement, a refrained singer or imaginative storyteller was always most welcome and came into 'their own' at such gatherings.

My grandmother having no other claims on the world regarding skills or fame, apart from rearing a large family in decency and hard work - 'there was never a bad word said against her' - was such a storyteller.

However, ghostly tales seemed to far outweigh the humorous yarns and was it any wonder that I suffered so many nightmares in that dark bricked house? For at times the occupants seemed to be as much in the next world as in this one.

They spoke of the past; of past lives, past loves, past events, and talked of the dead as if they were still alive. As a child I would listen to their conversations and strange tales and think of it all as quite normal as I believed that all adults talked about ghosts and haunted houses. Their ghostly happenings always seemed to involve the speakers themselves and not hearsay or gathered from magazines, but real personal experiences. Some, to my terror, had even taken place in or near that quiet little street near the centre of Belfast.

'Willy's Drowning' was one of those strange tales that became part of the family history.

Willy, her seaman son, was sending money home to a girl he wished to marry. One day he arrived home after many months at sea to find her either married, or about to be, to someone else, the money spent or gone. At this point in the story I always wondered about the money for I never had any, except for what I was given for running 'messages' to the corner shop. However, to a heartbroken and spurned lover the money was unimportant and Willy fled back to sea. He was once asked why he never married and his excuse was always, 'The good girls don't want me and I don't want the bad ones!' Before he set out on his last voyage, a gypsy woman came to the door and feeling the bumps

and hollows on his head said, 'You'll drown at sea'.

Which, on reflection, was very honest and brave of the woman as they usually only relate good omens like, my grandmother's tea leaves, of money and good fortune. Like all carefree spirits, Willy laughed it off and said life should be short and sweet. Those remarks were always my grandmother's prelude to the strange tale she told.

One night my grandmother awoke in her bedroom to hear Willy drowning, she could hear the water gurgling in his throat, his choking, spluttering gasps and him sobbing her name. In the darkness of the bedroom she'd sat upright shivering in a cold sweat, listening but utterly helpless to the last gasps of a favourite son as his life slipped away in those oily waters of a foreign harbour halfway around the world.

As a natural born storyteller, she'd mimic every gurgling word and sound, finishing her recollection with Willy calling her name, before his lungs filled with water. A strange tale that never failed to capture everyone's attention, and as her friend Lil Rooney once said, 'Surely the truth for what mother would make up a story like that about her son's death?'

That dreadful night's experience was confirmed by the inevitable telegram, of which she already knew contents before opening. All she ever received was his chief steward's uniform, and that was quickly disposed off for it only added to her grief. She must have been an emotionally strong woman for life went on - no doctor, no breakdown, no taking to her bed. She had great faith in life after death, ghosts and strange happenings were all common occurrences to her.

I once asked her was she not afraid of ghosts, for she always seemed to be seeing or hearing them.

'No! Sure the dead can do ye no harm, it's only the living that harm ye.'

I'd strongly disagreed for the dead could scare the living daylights out of ye!

It was after such late nights listening to the tea cups being 'read' or the latest sighting of some ghostly 'shade' or wraith, that I'd lie awake at night huddled under a heavy patchwork quilt, my young ears straining for the slightest sound on the wooden stairs leading to my room. It being an old house rarely was I disappointed, my helplessness and terror compounded by the indifference of my aunt in the next room snoring her head off!

Now the obituary column of the Belfast Telegraph was the first and sometimes the only part of the paper my grandmother ever read. Most nights she would call to my aunt: 'Do you know who's dead?'

So I'd lie awake thinking to myself, if my grandmother is so unafraid of ghosts and knows so many who are dead, wouldn't it be just like one of those dead ones that had nothing better to do but to think of paying her a visit. Darkness and fear were forming in my imagination so that every dark corner could conceal some sinister shape. My dark isolation was only broken by the all-too-brief passing of a solitary car as its friendly lights raced across the wall and ceiling. I'd lay awake until the grey dawn chased away the dark shapes from the shadows and I'd finally close my eyes for the last few hours before I rose for school.

Yes, I remember those quiet wet Sundays and I'm thankful to have known such good people who, having a young one thrust upon them in their later years, did the best they could. They gave me an insight into an older, less materialistic perception of life and death. Socially, with their 'visiting' and 'wakes' and the communal sharing of their hardships, they were more 'alive' than many are today.

To my old guardians death was part of life, something to be faced and talked about. It wasn't a subject to hide and show discomfort with when it was mentioned.

Yes, I'm thankful for those quiet times, but in truth, I wished they'd sent me off earlier to bed when I was very young before the cups were read and they spoke in whispers of the recent dead.

REQUIEM FOR A PRINCE

By MARIE GAHAN
Greenhills, Dublin

*Young and newly married, her 'Prince' was a constant companion
and helped her to overcome the odds and become competent at
her home making duties.*

I'll never forget my first gas cooker; it was a Parkinson Cowan
Prince. On a cloud of pre-wedding euphoria, I chose it one
day in my lunch hour. All pristine white and shiny, it cost the
princely sum of thirty seven pounds; worth every penny with
it's eye-level grill, very trendy for 1969. I was excited. My first
appliance would be in readiness in our new home when I moved
in with my brand new husband. I visualised myself serving him
mouth-watering meals each evening when he arrived home.

I had to leave my job when I married. In today's egalitarian
society, my daughters are   incensed on my account, but I
didn't have an option at that time. But being at home all day
allowed plenty of time to get to know my new Prince. I missed
my friends in the office; several of them country girls who had
learned to cater for themselves in shabby bedsits. Like all young
Dubliners at the time, I lived at home with my parents until
marriage. Looking back now, I realise I took every meal handed
to me for granted. My world revolved around music, dancing
and showbands.

Although I wouldn't admit it for the world, I was secretly in
awe of my first appliance. A complete novice to cooking, I feared
I might burn the house down with it or even give my beloved
an ulcer. From my venerable position as a grandmother today,
I can afford to laugh at my ineptitude and sympathise with the
young girl I was, who found domesticity so daunting.

As I stood in my kitchen in my Mary Quant miniskirt, I was very apprehensive about my shortcomings in the culinary arts. I opened the gleaming oven door and found a manual. It gave recipes and vivid pictures of all the delicious dishes that could be achieved on grill, oven and hob. Happy days! They made it sound so easy. So I rolled up my sleeves and got stuck in.

The vagaries of a cooker had never darkened my brow before. But now, all of a sudden, here I was, a juggler trying to keep all the balls in the air. Only they weren't balls; they were pots on the hob. As I concentrated on frying steak in the pan, I forgot to lower the temperature under the potatoes and they ended up in mush. Just as everything was piping hot, and I was about to dish up, I suddenly realized I had let the gas go out under the vegetables, and they were still raw.

The secrets we shared, my Prince and I, in that first year as a very young housewife. The flops that went straight from oven to bin in the early days; nobody knew about them but us. Same with the pots that burned dry as I answered the bell and ended up chatting on the doorstep, oblivious to the burning smell down the hall. The sponges that flopped in the middle, the spillages, when I forgot to lower the temperature for the simmering rice, the lumpy sauces and custards – all these remained secrets between just my prince and me.

To his credit, my new husband bore my culinary apprenticeship like a true stoic. There was never the teeniest complaint, or reproof. Without a word, he'd set to with Brillo pad and elbow grease to undo the havoc I had wrought on my shiny new pots, and I loved him all the more for it. Eventually his patience was rewarded. Little by little, I got more adept at my task.

My confidence grew with each successful meal. By the time my first baby arrived, I was in full control. Nowadays, I enjoy baking gingerbread men for my little grandsons. They love my fruit slices and Victoria sponge and want me to teach them how to bake. Life has turned full circle.

My loyal Prince served me well for fifteen years and never once let me down. By then we were a little more affluent and could afford a modern fitted kitchen. The workmen insisted that its sleek lines demanded the very latest split level oven and hob. After all, they pointed out; my Prince was showing signs of wear and tear.

It looked so homely and out of place amid the sophistication of its modern setting that I decided to take their advice and abandon the faithful friend that had withstood my abuse and seen me through a vital learning curve.

But I didn't reckon on how fond I had become of it over the years. Memories flooded back and I felt like a traitor as they took it away. After forty years I've had to replace many things in my home, but to this day I still hanker after the cooker I cut my bridal teeth on; my Parkinson Cowan, a true Prince among appliances.

Beginners Short Story Runner-Up

Cuts Like a Knife

By Doreen Duffy

Clondalkin, Dublin

Paddy and Ellen worked hard and hoped to provide for their only son all the things they'd had to do without.

It was Friday, the day for collecting his pension. Patrick Michael Dwyer, Paddy, went through his normal routine. Up early, washed and dressed, his neat white short hair combed, his soft cap given a little tug to secure it into position. He ran his hand across his square jaw, rough, packed tight with short sharp bristles and buttoned the collar of his shirt to keep out the cold in the absence of a tie.

He opened the kitchen drawer and took out the long pointed silver handled knife, the blade so sharp that he always took care to return it to its safe resting place after use. The weight of its handle pressed into his hand, the engraving rough under his fingers.

He went into the hall and as always placed the point of the knife into the lock of the old hall table; he jiggled the knife and heard the lock turn as the drawer slid open to reveal the small pile of money. He took what he would need and when he twisted the knife backwards to re lock it, his mind suddenly threw up memories so nasty and sour that he breathed deeply through gritted teeth as they started to play out like a film across the screen of his mind.

His wife Ellen was at the table slicing open the post one morning with the sharp silver handled knife. He was watching her remembering when her Father had given the knife to him, presented it to him really. His father-in-law had told Paddy it was quite valuable, a special find and he wanted to pass it on to him. Paddy treasured it as the only precious gift ever given to him. The fact that his father-in-law wanted him to have it meant more to him than the value of the knife. Paddy wasn't used to being given things, especially something of value.

He had been born on the outskirts of Dublin and sent further into the city to live with an aunt and uncle at age thirteen for a promised job as a runner for a rag and bone man. He took his job seriously – no other way to take it in those days. He knew someone else would have the job by five o'clock if he messed up at 4.00 o'clock. Paddy worked very hard. He knew he was lucky to have ended up working for such a fair man who treated him so well.

When he was eighteen he felt blessed to have been allowed to accompany his employer's daughter Ellen to the 'Dance' in town on Saturday nights. They fell very much in love and married. After some time they had a son, James Michael, he was the centre of their world. They couldn't have been happier. Paddy continued to work his way up in his father-in-law's business and when the time came that his father-in-law died, he passed the business on to him.

Times had changed but business was good in the rag trade. James grew up so differently to Paddy, everything handed to him, nothing was too good for him but he ended up spoilt and selfish, he had no part of the personality of his parents. When he left home the only times they heard from him was when he was looking for money.

This particular day when Ellen sliced open one of the letters Paddy heard her gasp. He looked over her shoulder and read the letter written in their son James's scrawled handwriting, insisting that they send him more money, saying they wouldn't see him again if they didn't send the money. Paddy swore under his breath, rage catching suddenly in his throat and his hand shook as he took the letter out of her hand.

This wasn't the first time, he had come home one other day a little earlier than usual and heard shouting, realising the raised voice was his son's he hurriedly opened the door and rushed inside. Ellen was at the kitchen table clearly distraught, her ravaged face soaked with tears while James stood over her, fists clenched, face contorted with rage.

'He's come back again, he's looking for more money, I keep telling him there's nothing in the house, he won't listen Paddy, please tell him, tell him.'

Paddy couldn't believe what sort of person they had reared. Their only child that he'd held in his arms as a newborn, with such high hopes, he'd felt such sheer joy on the birth of a son. So loved and adored, they had given him everything and they had received only heartache in return and now this, threatening letters.

Paddy had left the house that day in a foul temper. The letter balled up deep in his pocket. He saw that gang of teenagers across the road, hanging around as always. Usually he spent a lot of his time questioning how they could afford the mobile phones, especially that young fella, couldn't be more than fourteen, always in that grey hooded top and dirty blue jeans. But this day even the sight of those young idle teenagers couldn't distract him from his rage.

As he went about his business he could feel his heart banging inside his chest, he knew he should try and calm down; his doctor had given him plenty of warnings about his increasingly weak heart. The evidence of sheer selfishness of his son was pumping boiling blood around his body, crashing in his ears. On the way home he had to stop walking, put his shopping down and lean against the wall at the top of his road, then he saw that gang across the road and the young fella approaching him.

'Hey mister,' he said,

Paddy tried to ignore him, he could feel his breathing starting to ease, he pushed his weight up off the wall but the boy kept on talking. 'D'you need a hand?'

He picked up the bags of shopping and started to walk towards Paddy's house. 'I've seen you around here before; I live up in the flats.'

Paddy said he knew his face from hanging around the streets. The young boy looked defensive

'Yeah, well, I try and stay out of the flat, my Da's not working and you never know when he's going to come home worse for wear and start throwing digs around.'

Paddy nodded, taking his bags, muttered thanks and let himself into the house, locking the door behind him.

It almost killed Paddy to watch as Ellen became increasingly sad and withdrawn. She became ill, very ill, TB they told Paddy. He tried to make contact with James to ask him to come home, he begged and he pleaded.

'James, you'll have it all, you'll have a good business to take over after I'm gone. It would mean so much to your mother,' his voice dropped, 'to me as well,' he said, 'things could be different it'd be a clean slate.'

'I have a life of my own, a good life, I'm doing some real living I'm not going to be stuck in the back end of nowhere, going nowhere. You won't catch me working myself into the ground the way you did. Just tell Mam I'm busy,' he said and hung up the phone.

Ellen seemed to sink away from him day by day. Paddy took care of her as best he could and he was grateful to be there to hold her as she passed away one night. Paddy still believed she died of a broken heart.

Paddy shook himself out of his very sad reverie and went out to collect his pension. At the top of the road there was that group of teenagers. As he neared them the young fella said 'How'ya Mister.'

Paddy nodded, 'maybe he's not such a bad lot after all,' he thought. It must be rough having a father like that throwing his weight around when he's full up with drink. Shaking his head as he walked on an old saying came to his mind,

'You can't choose your family'.

On the way home Paddy called into the pub and sat with the rest of the old timers at the bar. As usual they were talking about their families, sons, daughters, grachildren. Paddy joined in, said James was doing very well across the water, too busy to get home too often. Same old story every time, never portraying the deep anger he felt for his self-absorbed son. Any conversation was better than none he thought, in any case there was no rush to get home; it was a momentary relief from the loneliness.

When he arrived home and went into his house he saw the long pointed silver handled knife lying on the bottom of the stairs. He knew he had put it away earlier. He turned and saw the drawer in the hall table hanging open and bare. He heard movement upstairs, he picked up the smooth cold knife but Paddy couldn't believe the shock that awaited him when he reached the top of the stairs. He saw James, he was rifling through the chest of drawers where Ellen had kept her jewellery, stuffing boxes and necklaces into a bag. James turned and saw his father; the look that passed across his face was not contrite.

'I'm taking what's mine now old man, I'm not waiting any more, you'd take it with you if you could.'

Paddy heard the clash of the heavy cold metal hit the floor as he dropped the knife.

James pushed his father, warned him to get back downstairs, or else. Stunned and sick with horror at what his son was doing Paddy stumbled down the stairs. He could feel his chest tightening, pain slashing across it, his breath catching, he'd left the front door open in his haste to check upstairs and as he stepped out into the street a face appeared, a young face framed by a scruffy grey hood

'What's up mister, you okay?' he asked and caught Paddy as he started to crumple down to the ground. Relief swept over Paddy that someone was there to help him, and he stammered out that he was being robbed. The young lad took out his mobile phone and held Paddy as he called for an ambulance and said they'd need to send the Guards as well.

Just then James flew through the open doorway clutching the now bulging bag, the scruffy youth leapt up and grabbed him around the back of his neck and shoved him to the ground, two of his mates turned the corner,

'You all right Johnny?' they said and jumped in on top, pinning James to the ground. The ambulance arrived noisily to the scene, a Garda car pulling in behind it. Johnny pulled the bag out of James's hand and put it under Paddy's arm on the stretcher.

'You'll be alright now mister, they'll sort you out and we'll keep an eye on your place till your home.'

Paddy nodded and whispered 'Mmy name's Paddy...son.'

THE VISITATION

BY JAMES DEE

Ferbane, Co. Offaly.

Why small boys with big ears and bigger imaginations shouldn't listen to confusing adult conversations!

It was Easter 1959 and I was thinking about Visitations as I cycled home from school. Visitation is a big religious word used by priests and teachers but my mother had taken to using it lately and I was confused. Grown-ups had a habit of confusing small boys and my mother was no different.

I learned all about Visitations in school and they were to do with Holy God or His Blessed Mother; but it was mostly to do with the Mother for she seemed to do all the visiting on her own. I thought this was peculiar because when my mother went visiting she brought me with her, but Mrs. Holy God always left her little boy at home.

Grown-ups were strange.

The word had a fine ring to it. I practiced saying it as I free-wheeled past Kirby's. I was still repeating it as I passed Coleman's but only got it to sound right at the bottom of White's Hill. This was not a word invented for saying on bicycles or around at home but my mother had begun using it anyway. Was it because she had a nephew in the Christian Brothers or two brothers working in Glenstal Abbey?

Then, yesterday, she said it again. I heard her tell my Dad that she'd had a Visitation earlier that day! My ears opened wide.

Dad didn't seem at all excited about it. Amazingly, he kept chewing his dinner and just said 'Ooh' with his mouth full of bacon and cabbage. I was excited enough for both of us and cocked my ear for more. I knew already that such things happened to Shepherds in hot countries. But a Visitation at Cappanuke where it never stopped raining was a different thing entirely!

Mother carried on with her story as if this was a normal thing to happen at our house.

'There I was,' she was saying, kneeling down to clean the fireplace and when I turned around 'Herself' was standing right there, near the table.'

Mam paused to light a cigarette. Dad stopped chewing and I stayed very quiet.

'I never heard her come in the door; she just appeared miraculously behind me.'

Mam pointed to a spot on the linoleum between the fireplace and the table. A cold chill ran down my nine year old spine. That part of the floor looked no different from the day before but there had to be some change, for after all a Miraculous Visitation had taken place at that very spot just a few hours earlier.

I studied the Lino for a sign because my teacher said there was always something left behind after Miraculous Visitations. Sure enough it was a bit worn right there. Was that because holy feet had touched it?

Boys, oh boys!

Just as well my Mam was on her knees when The Visitation happened, even if it was just cleaning out the fireplace.

Dad raised his right eyebrow in that special way he had when he was too busy to ask a question.

'Herself' the eyebrow asked?

'You know well who I'm talking about...HERSELF, from up above Cappamore,' Mam said impatiently, nodding towards the back wall of the kitchen, east, toward that two - street Metropolis.

Heaven was up above Cappamore? So that's where it was! I had always suspected as much for that village had a cinema AND the annual circus. The place was practically a city. They already had everything and now owned Heaven too. Compared to Cappamore our little village was a mere dot on the landscape with only a hurling field and an old monument to boast of. And there was me thinking all along that Heaven was up over Glenstal Abbey.

Quickly I wondered where Hell was. It was hardly anywhere near Cappamore and that's for sure. Oh no, THEY wouldn't want it, so it was probably deep down under Murroe somewhere, but not up near Holy Glenstal of course. Maybe Hell really was under Willie Maloney's Quarry just like Dad said when I was small. Just then he managed to say something.

'And what did she want...THIS time?'

THIS TIME!

My mind ran riot. This had happened before? So SHE was a regular Visitationer to our kitchen. No wonder that patch of Lino was worn. I didn't know whether to be proud or afraid and couldn't wait for the reply.

Dad was waiting too, a bit of slippery fat bacon dangling from the dinner fork poised halfway to his mouth.

Mam shook her head sadly. 'She came to tell me that her ass was dead...they found the poor thing this morning up at the end of the field.'

Now things were getting confused.

Holy God's Mother had come on A Miraculous Visitation to Cappanuke to tell MY mother that their ass was dead! Surely the ass Holy God and his Blessed Mother owned was dead long before now, at least a hundred years, but he only died that very morning and Holy God's Mother wouldn't tell a lie.

I wondered what age the ass was and how he managed to live so long. I was puzzled too as to why Holy God didn't just bring him back to life instead of sending HIS Mother to tell MY mother about it.

Was this was another Sorrowful Mystery I'd have to remember at the Rosary?

Dad was shaking his head and seemed to be thinking along those very same lines.

'T'was not before his time I suppose, and 'tis a mystery he lasted so long with the bad grass they have up there... anyway, he must have been as old as Methuselah himself. I'll bet she came all the way down here for a loan of ours,' he added, placing the piece of bacon in his mouth at last.

How could the man eat at a time like this?

This was big stuff indeed so I tried to get it all straight in my head.

Holy God's ass was dead and He sent His Mother to borrow ours. My mind couldn't take it in. But why did HERSELF pick OUR house?

Everyone around Cappanuke had an ass and what was so special about ours; or 'Stubborn Eedjit' as Dad called him? He'd hardly be able for a Flight into Egypt, if that's what they wanted him for. Anyway, our old ass wouldn't know the way because my Dad said he was too stupid to find his way home from the Union Bog. And that was just behind our house.

How would God's Mother get an ass up to Heaven and then back down again; or... would she bring him back at all? Besides, our ass was alive and everyone knew you had to be dead before getting in the Gate up there. I was told that when someone went to Heaven they stayed for a long time, hundreds of years even, and now our ass was needed up there.

Would Stubborn Eedjit be gone 'Forever and Ever Amen' as Canon Kennedy says during Mass in Murroe? Up to then I never knew asses went to Heaven, dead or alive. Was that because the grass wasn't any good up there? A tear for Stubborn Eedjit formed in the corner of my eye and ran down my freckly nose before I could stop it.

These were big questions but I was sure Holy Gods Mother had thought of a way of getting our ass back home. That is, if my Dad let her take him at all.

Mam lit another Woodbine and blew a puff towards The Miraculous Visitation Holy Worn Spot on the Lino. The rest of the smoke formed a ring above her head just like the halos over Saints in the windows of Murroe Church.

'I already gave her the loan of our ass...and the winkers too, an' Herself said Old Joe would drop him back sometime tonight,' Mam was saying, casual as you like. 'OLD JOE?' Old Joe! So that was what they called him up there in Heaven! Of course WE had to call him by his proper name, Saint Joseph, and he was going to drop our ass back into our field. Tonight! Boys, oh boys!

I wouldn't want to miss that. It would be better than any circus trick in Cappamore!

Last night I stayed awake as long as I could to hear the noise of an ass being dropped into our field all the way down from Holy God's house high up above Cappamore. I prayed that Saint Joseph had a good aim because the field was small and I didn't want Stupid Eedjit landing in the Union Bog.

I must have fallen asleep and missed it for this morning there was Stupid Eedjit grazing happily when I got up for school. He didn't look any the worse for his trip up to Heaven, or the fright at being dropped back down. I looked closely and saw the cross was still on his back and I was glad.

Dad said something about us being very lucky if that Cappamore crowd didn't take it before we got him back. The Winkers hung neatly on the Gate- post and I was doubly impressed.

Boys oh boys!

Old Saint Joe was a real good shot and I couldn't wait to tell my teacher all about it.

THE SCOTCHIES FORTNIGHT

By VINCENT J. DOHERTY
Palmer's Green, London

*August was that special time when many of those who had
emigrated to Scotland came back home for an escape from reality.*

August was a special time when I was a boy, the best time
of the year except when it was Christmas or it snowed.
The sun blazed out of a clear blue sky all our waking
hours and cares and school could have been a thousand miles
away.

I remember in particular those mornings of anticipation when
I woke early and ran out into the still dewy field by the side of
our house. From there I could see for miles on a morning like
that. Away across the Foyle valley the sun was lifting the mist
off the hills of Donegal.

I would stand there watching and waiting impatiently on
the edge of the ditch for the Great Northern out of Derry to
come steaming through Porthall, carrying our Scotchies to
Strabane Station. Then Danny Connolly would bring them the
last four miles or so from there to us in his taxi, a rare car in the
countryside in those days of the early Fifties.

We were ready for the Scotchies. Everything was fresh. The
house was turned inside out from top to bottom, wallpapered,
whitewashed, varnished, distempered and Cardinal polished.
New linoleum was laid. There were tea roses round the door and
red geraniums on newly painted window sills behind spotless
windows and starched lace curtains..

The yard was brushed and I was scrubbed and suited at the
last minute.

The Scotchies were cousins of ours, McGettigans, Gallaghers
and Rices, the children and grandchildren of exiles who had

taken the boat to the Broomielaw a generation or so before. They were born and brought up in the crowded Glasgow tenements of Shettleston, Carntyne and Parkhead.

They had lived all their lives there and they would grow old there but they lived with the dream of coming home to a farm like ours, even if it was only a hilly, back breaking few acres with a cow. They had visions of small fertile farms, open roads, harvest fields, heathery mountains, bogs strewn with bog cotton, dry turf stacks and the seemingly comfortable summer life of country people.

And every August for a fortnight they would leave the fumes of the city and their sweated labour in the foundries, laundries and factories and with heads and hearts full of glad anticipation make their way 'home' on the Derry boat.

They swapped their running water for the water carried from our spring well and electricity for the light from an Aladdin paraffin lamp. They swapped their trams for Shanks' Pony and their Ration Books for sweet milk warm from the cow, buttermilk and butter straight from the churn, eggs from the nest and potatoes they could dig straight out of the earth and eat with fresh herrings from Killybegs.

They would happily walk miles to dance in country dance halls

We welcomed our visitors fulsomely. My mother would lay out a big spread for their arrival. There was fresh oilcloth on the table and her best linen tablecloth laid and smoothed over that. The bone china was brought out of its shrine in the glass- fronted cabinet. There was baked soda bread and a big fry. There was homemade jam and sweet tea you could stand a spoon up in.

There was news to be exchanged. They brought with them an exciting foreign world. They spoke what sounded like another language and produced a cornucopia of comics and Annuals - Black Bob and Superman- and news of the triumphs of Glasgow Celtic. They brought company.

Normality and the solitary existence of an only child would be postponed for the next fortnight. There were silver florins to be had and the promise of fish suppers and ice cream in glass dishes in Vacarro's Italian ice cream parlour.

Sometimes there was a carnival in aid of the school building fund. There would be rides on dodgem cars and chairoplanes, prizes to be won at the hoopla stall.

With a cow and calves and hens to be fed and seven acres for a living there was precious little time for excursions but now there would be excursions on a Sunday. First to early morning Mass, then on to a bus and away to Bundoran for digging the sand, paddling, pastries and a new straw hat. There might be outings in cars in the evenings, or the pictures, late nights and long country walks.

But a fortnight doesn't last forever. Soon enough, as the nights drew in, the time for parting came and with heavy hearts on solemn Saturday evenings my father and I went with them to Derry and the boat.

We waved to them from the quay and they waved back as they sailed into the distance of Lough Foyle in the direction of home and reality.

THE RING

^{BY} CARMEL B. ROY

Palmer's Green, London

Mary is in trouble as her anniversary looms – she has lost her treasured wedding ring and has not told her husband the bad news.

It had long been their dream to return to Ireland from Glasgow, but it was when Mary got the chance of early retirement that it suddenly became possible. Eamonn was already free of what had become the tyranny of work with its relentless routine and the increasing number of over-confident young teachers in the department.

Their easy way with the ever-changing technology had gradually eroded his confidence and he noticed that the children he taught seemed to inhabit a world he no longer recognised. He had felt that he was becoming invisible, a sad contrast to the energetic and innovative teacher of his younger days.

When Mary, her eyes shining at the thought of a new life, told Eamonn the news he looked relieved. He hadn't wanted to tell Mary of the emptiness that had descended on his days following retirement, but in truth, without his job he had lost his identity.

'Well, what do you think? Shall I accept the offer?' she asked.

To her surprise, tears came to Eamonn's eyes and he drew her gently towards him to conceal his emotion. The tears, however, were not lost on Mary, as she had been concerned for months at his apparent lack of interest in life. Yes, he still enjoyed his crossword in the favourite easy chair by the kitchen window, but close friends had moved to be near grandchildren, and Saturday football games were no longer a feature of what had once been his busy week.

'Let's go back to Ireland to live', he murmured into her hair.

The weeks following Mary's leaving 'do' were filled with action and anticipation. Mary and Eamonn began to experience the delight of keen excitement which they could not recall feeling since their young days when they had packed for holidays in Cork with their two children.

The small house in the countryside and near the beach they had inherited from an uncle long since and had visited each Summer, doing their best to keep it from being taken over by nature and worn away by the elements. Its large garden was going to be a challenge but they thought they could manage it, and maybe grow vegetables to help them survive on the smaller budget of pensioners.

The top floor flat in Glasgow that they had loved was now a source of problems. Taking the bin down all those stairs had become a major chore; carrying heavy bags of shopping up was worse; and Mary had always wanted a garden she could step into in the mornings, just wearing her nightie and dressing gown if she wanted to.

The view of the West End from the kitchen window with its church spires, Victorian tenement roofs and the hills beyond, no longer inspired them. Looking out at the twinkling lights of the city the night before they left for Cork, Mary realised that she wasn't going to miss it. And now that the children were settled and happy - Bella with her kind and caring Dan, and Niall with lovely Helen - she knew she was ready for the next stage.

It was early spring when they waved the removal van off and watched it drive under the archway of ash trees and out of sight. In the house there was an undeniable smell of damp and they looked in dismay at the stacks of boxes. They hardly knew where to start, but after a short hesitation Mary said, 'Right, a cup of tea and then we can make up the bed. It's too late to start unpacking now'.

Waking the next morning Eamonn didn't know where he was for a moment, then he heard the rhythmic trotting of next door's ponies as they passed the house and remembered. Pulling on his dressing gown he ducked to avoid the low door lintel and was half way down the stairs when he smelled the mouth-watering rashers that Mary was just putting on the kitchen table.

'Where did this soda bread come from?' he enquired, watching his wife cutting it into generous slices on the wooden breadboard. 'Yes, I've been dying to tell you. The people from the farm across the valley called early to welcome us, and brought you some whiskey too', she replied with a smile. The kindness touched them both and seemed to confirm that they had made the right decision in coming home to live.

Over the next weeks and months they rejoiced at being able to watch the changing seasons. First the winding lanes were edged with sunny dandelions, to be replaced by wild violets and primroses, and in the summer with lines of purple loose- strife against a pink backdrop of wild roses. Then autumn brought its bounty of apples, blackberries and plump black sloes.

As they drove slowly to the nearby town drinking in the yellowing beech trees, and the hawthorns embroidered with their russet berries sparked with dew, they felt a deep gratitude for the freedom to take their time and enjoy their new surroundings. They both felt more alive than they had for a long while, and found time to join a swimming club and a film society as well as setting the house and garden to rights.

There was just one thing that clouded Mary's happiness and that was the loss of her wedding ring. She had been washing up, admiring the tall white flowers of the Cosmos from the scullery window as they waved back and forth in the wind, when she glanced down at her red hands in the bubbles and saw it was gone. Instantly panic took hold as her mind raced back over her day and the possible places she could have lost it.

She had been shopping, and had called in at the library to return her books; she'd trawled through the bric-a-brac in a couple of charity shops, and stood on the footbridge over the river to watch the grey heron flop lazily across the weir. Where on earth had she lost it?

She'd definitely had it on that morning as she remembered fingering it as she wrote the shopping list. The mystery was that, as she had never taken it off since the day Eamonn had placed it on her finger, she couldn't imagine what had happened to it.

It's true, she and Eamonn had been very sentimental about the ring and Mary had entertained a vague notion that when the ring came off, the marriage would be over. Once or twice in heated arguments she had considered wrenching it off her finger and throwing it back at him but this was long ago and she had always thought better of it.

The memory of her silly superstition filled her with disquiet as she mentally rehearsed telling him, imagining his disappointed look. Being short of money at the time of their wedding, he had sold his beloved motorbike to buy it for her, and this had convinced her of the strength of his feeling. It truly was irreplaceable.

She recalled how it had been engraved with delicate ivy leaves all around it, before nappy washing and housework had worn their beauty away.

Days and weeks passed and, strangely, Eamonn failed to notice that she was no longer wearing the precious ring. She hunted around the garden, even turning up the last flower bed she'd been working on the day it had disappeared. She rummaged in the out-house through the remaining boxes from the removal; she retraced her steps of that unlucky day, searching through the bric-a-brac in Gorta and the other charity shops.

Once, she stood on the footbridge again and prayed to Saint Anthony as she gazed down into the water, but all she could discern was a solitary trout swimming against the current and not making any progress.

She was reminded of the story of St. Mungo on the Glasgow coat-of-arms. A queen had given a handsome soldier a ring that had been the gift of her king, but the king noticed its absence and, suspecting duplicity, commanded her to wear it. Terrified, she asked St Mungo for help and taking pity on her, he told a man to fish in the river and the salmon he caught had the ring inside it.

'Well, my king hasn't even noticed' thought Mary, 'Yet'.

Their thirtieth wedding anniversary was approaching, a fact that put dread in Mary's heart. Surely it would be impossible to hide it from Eamonn that day of all days. The afternoon before, she scoured the town again for anything that could trigger a memory that would help restore the wedding ring to the finger that looked naked without it.

She decided to confide in Maureen, a friend she'd made at the film club, who she'd arranged to meet for coffee. Maureen, small and neat with a warm smile, found Mary huddled at a corner table looking miserable.

'How are ye, girl? You look like you've lost a pound and found a penny.'

Tears pricked Mary's eyes in the telling for she couldn't help feeling that there was no hope, and Maureen listened sympathetically as the story came tumbling out. Finally, Mary blew her nose and was quiet.

'Well, the best advice I can give is to tell Eamonn. He'll be the first to understand that these things happen and it's not the end of the world. You're still a happy couple so don't allow this to spoil your anniversary tomorrow.' Maureen said gently. 'Anyway, if Saint Anthony couldn't help then you'll just have to give up,' she added, smiling kindly.

Mary didn't sleep well that night, and her dreams were full of fish and tangled fishing lines, with a heron always stealing the catch. She awoke to the sound of Eamonn drawing the curtains, and the delicious aroma of fresh coffee.

'Breakfast milady', joked Eamonn. 'And a very happy anniversary to you!' She sat up and accepted the breakfast tray with feigned delight. She didn't want to spoil their special day, but she knew that he must be told.

'Eamonn, I have to tell you something...' she forced out the words.

'No, my best girl, he replied affectionately, 'not before you've seen your anniversary present'.

He lifted the napkin on the tray and watched her face light up when she saw the lost ring sitting between her boiled egg, and a small green box.

'What the...Where did you find it?'

'Never mind that just now, don't you want to look in the box?'

Mary hesitantly lifted its lid to be met by the flash and sparkle of a wonderful diamond in what could only be described as an engagement ring.

They embraced warmly and he apologised for allowing her to worry about the wedding ring, and then explained that he'd found it in her gardening glove that fateful day.

'I needed it to get your ring size so that I could get you the engagement ring you never had', he said gently. 'I always intended to set the situation to rights but what with the children and work I just never got around to it. I knew you'd never take it off so it was a godsend when I found you'd pulled it off with your glove. You must have lost a bit of weight with all that gardening.'

'Imagine you thinking I hadn't noticed', he added, cheekily dipping some toast in her egg'.

Mary didn't answer, but as he carried the breakfast tray from the room she whispered fervently, 'Thank you, Saint Anthony'.

HIGHLY COMMENDED

Hanging In There

By Agnes Kimberley

Port Elizabeth, South Africa

*Sometimes a ray of sunshine brightens even the
gloomiest situations.*

'Sixty.' I thought, 'Sixty years old. I wonder how many years
I've got left. If you're listening God, if they're going to be as
miserable as the last five, I don't want many more!

'Come back to me, James,' I said out loud, looking at the
empty space in the bed. 'Come back to me, keep me company
for whatever's left, okay.'

The silence was all around me. It was an eerie quiet. It was
like opening a book to read, only to discover that there were
no words written on the pages. I hated the quietness that filled
my life these days. I dressed in silence, ate my meals alone in
silence, and lay all alone in my bed with nothing but silence
surrounding me.

Where once I would have given my eye teeth for a bit of peace
and quiet, I was now lonely and uncomfortable in its presence.
And to make matters worse, I'd begun waking up every morning
at three o'clock. At first I'd twist and turn and try and go back
to sleep, but only ended up getting a massive headache for my
efforts. I'd creep around the house like a thief in the night. I
could have put the TV or radio on, but the noise did nothing
to lift the heaviness from my heart. And I, who used to love
nothing more than reading, just couldn't concentrate on the
words. I had nothing to distract me.

It was exactly one year today that our darling Aileen had
been taken from us. James had been with me then. We had
three fine, strapping sons and then when I was nearly forty, I
discovered I was pregnant. The whole family was thrilled when
I had a daughter. Aileen had three older brothers to spoil her,
not to mention her doting parents.

'I'd give anything to see you rock her to sleep, just one more time, James,' I cried softly to myself.

Never for a moment had anyone thought that there was anything wrong with her. It was Michael, my eldest son, who said to me one day, 'Mum, I think you should take Aileen to the doctor.'

I had never seen him look so serious. 'She never cries.' He looked expectantly at me.

'Go on,' I urged him, as bile rose into my mouth.

'She has no interest in anything around her. She stares at the wall for hours.'

I remember standing there and thinking what a great father he'd make and I told him so.

'Thanks Mum,' he grinned at me. 'That won't be happening for a good while yet. I want to finish school first.'

'Of course you do, but you'll still make a great father one day.'

'Do you want me to go to the doctor with you, Mum?'

'No, it's alright son. You've got your exams coming up.'

Aileen was six months old then.

'Are you sure you can handle this alone, Mum?'

I kissed him on the cheek. 'Stop fussing, darling. I'll be fine. Where is Aileen now?'

'She's in my room. She fell asleep on my bed.'

'Well, in that case I'll make a start on dinner. Your dad and brothers will be home shortly.'

'Alright Mum,' Michael nodded his head.

We didn't love her any less when we found out she had been deprived of oxygen at some point during my delivery. Her brain would never pass the level of a six-year-old. It was hard to accept at first and God alone knows I raged against Him, but in time I accepted what He had given me. When it was time to send her to school we enrolled her in a special school.

The years rolled on and, one by one, the boys left home. They all attended university, got married and, soon after, they had their own children. Then, there were only the three of us left in the house. James was marvellous with Aileen. She loved the beach and it became the place where we'd bring our joys and sorrows. I planned on going to visit the beach today, but there was somewhere I had to go visit first.

James's accident happened nearly three months ago. It was almost nine months to the day that Aileen had died.

Sometimes I still get angry with God. I shout and rant at him in the silence of my mind. I keep asking him why He let this happen to me. I tell him I've been a good Christian all my life. I've never wronged anybody. I brought my family up with good morals. They had always been taught right from wrong.

'Why, why me?' I keep asking him, but I'm still waiting for an answer. 'Wasn't it enough you took my daughter?'

My husband should be here with me now. We should be enjoying growing old together. Then as soon as the anger bubbled up in me, it would start to fade. It took too much effort to stay angry for so long. Then I'd start to think where there's hope, there's a chance. And I can still hope and pray that he will recover and come back to me.

He has good days, bad days and very bad days. James is suffering from amnesia and most days are bad.

At first I'd thought, we'd all thought that he had been careless on the road. He'd been thinking of something else, still mourning his daughter's death. Aileen had been ill for some time before she died.

'It's a virus,' the doctor told us. 'We're doing all we can, but, as you know, her heart has always been weak.'

Soon after she began to recover and, just when we thought the worst was over, she got sick again. One night she just slipped silently away in her sleep.

James held me for a long time and together we mourned our precious daughter. Then my husband said the strangest thing to me.

'I know you'll think I'm being selfish saying this, but, of the three of us, you're the strongest, Maggie. I want to go before you do. Who would have cared for Aileen when our time is up? The tears poured out of his eyes and ran unchecked down his face.'

'He must have been suffering from terrible headaches,' the doctor at the hospital said to me. 'Blackouts, too. We did a scan and found a tumour right on the frontal lobe.'

'Brain tumour, blackouts, headaches,' I echoed. 'He never said a word to me.'

'More than likely he suffered a blackout when the car went off the road,' the doctor said softly. 'Thank God nobody else was injured.'

When I left the house, the sky was grey and the wind was bitterly cold. I made the two-hour round trip to the care facility three times a week.

After James was released from the hospital, I insisted he come home to me. I was strong and capable and I'd take good care of him. But my best wasn't good enough and I couldn't cope. The boys had called a family meeting and we had all discussed professional care. I had been appalled at first , but, finally, I realized it was the right thing to do.

'It's for the best,' Michael hugged me hard, and, of course, he was right.

James, who had never shown any anger, was now volatile and full of rage. Whereas before he was quiet and submissive, he could now easily smash the crockery from the dresser, tear the carpet to pieces, and run around the house naked brandishing a sharp knife in his hands.

He now wore a permanent scowl on his face where once there was only a smile. And he cried inconsolably for hours at a time. It was heartbreaking to witness it.

Now we, the family, visited as often as we could. The boys took it in turns to visit him on the days I didn't go. I always visited him on Tuesday, Thursday and Sunday.

'Hello darling,' I bent and kissed him on the cheek.

He looked at me as if I was a complete stranger. I swallowed the lump that formed in my throat. The nurses and doctors had warned me about not getting too emotional in front of him.

I made idle chit chat with him for a few minutes. I told him what the boys were up to and how the grand-kids were faring at school.

'Aileen,' he said suddenly. 'Where is she?'

'Aileen is ---.' I had no idea what to say.

But just as fleetingly as he got the memory it is gone. The blank look is back on his face again.

The nurse came in then and wheeled him out for lunch. They keep a strict routine at the hospital, otherwise the patients tend to get all worked up.

'Would you like some tea?' she asked me before she left.

'Yes, please,' I answered her with a smile.

My mobile rang in my bag.

'Happy birthday, Mum.' It was Michael.

'Thanks, son.'

'Are you with Dad? How is he?'

'Much the same,' I said with a heavy sigh.

No sooner had I drank my tea than the same nurse wheeled James back into the room. He wore an angry scowl on his face.

'What's wrong, sweetheart?' I asked as I helped the nurse put him into bed.

'We had chicken for dinner. I hate chicken,' he talked and acted like a three-year-old spoilt child.

'You've always liked chicken before.' I tried to calm him down.

'How on earth would you know what I liked?' he spat at me. 'I don't even know you.' He turned on his side and a moment later he began snoring softly.

I shook my head as the tears formed in the corner of my eyes. The nurse put a comforting hand around my shoulders.

'You know he doesn't mean it.'

'I know,' I said softly.

I have never been able to visit the graveyard where my precious daughter lies beneath the soil. The boys visit every week and put fresh flowers on it. They miss their sister terribly too.

Instead, I went to the beach. The beach had only good memories for me. Oh, how Aileen had loved frolicking in the water. She had adored building sand castles in the sand. In fact, she had loved everything about the sea.

Overhead, a seagull soared. I looked up at him.

'He's looking for crusts,' a voice said behind me.

'Michael! What on earth are you doing here?'

'I knew you'd be here.' He sat down crying, big tears rolling down his cheeks, his chest shaking as he tried to keep in the sobs.

'Darling! What is it? What's wrong?'

He wiped his eyes and looked with tenderness at me.

'Dad gave me this last week.' He put his hand in his pocket and extracted a small, white envelope. Wordlessly, I opened it and began to read the contents:

'Dear Maggie,

I'm having some very lucid thoughts now. I want to put them down on paper before my mind becomes fogged again.

I just want you to know that I love you very much. Please hang in there! I feel one day in the future, I'll slowly make my way back to you.

Your loving husband
    James'

'He knew it was your birthday today, Mum.'

Tears filled my eyes. I cried until there were no tears left.

'Dad asked me to buy sixty red roses for you.'

James had always given me red roses on my birthday. They were my favourite flowers.

My son leant down and pulled me up. Then arm in arm we walked across the sand and headed towards our cars.

'I'll see you at six, Mum,' he kissed me goodbye.

We were having a quiet family dinner.

'Dad is slowly making his way home,' he said.

'I know that son,' I felt a lightness in my heart that had not been there for a very long time.

ROSIE RETRIEVED

BY CATHERINE RHATIGAN

Eiglisau, Switzerland

*'Luke can do it,' they had said, and Luke was determined to do
his best if only he knew what to do.*

Luke loved Rosie. He loved her wonderful dark eyes and
their long lashes, her quiet lazy walk, how she smelled.
Every evening he waited for her at the end of the road,
happy to hear the steady sound of her feet on the path, and
when she came into view, he always went to her and gently put
his arms around her neck. For a moment, her felt her warm face
against his, then she would softly move away. He could tell her
anything, all the secrets of his heart, and he did, knowing she
would keep them to herself.

Luke had first seen her when he came to work on his uncle's
farm for the summer. It was a busy place, and very different
from the city where he lived, and in those first evenings it was
Rosie and her quietness that helped him adjust, overcome his
homesickness. Who would believe him if he said he was lonely
with all that work to do and all those noisy cousins around?
But he was.

He missed the sound of cars driving past at night in the
yellow light of the city street where he lived. He missed how a
city looks, the grey stain of rain on concrete and how a breeze
can flick around a bus shelter like a live thing. He missed his
room, his books on their shelves and his CD collection and all
his drawings. And, of course, he missed his parents.

Then came the evening that Rosie wasn't there. Luke went
as usual to the end of the road, tired and expectant, but no
Rosie. He waited ten minutes, before admitting to himself,
disappointed, that she wasn't coming.

'That's the women for you,' said his uncle cheerfully, 'there
one day and gone the next.'

'What are you talking about,' said his wife, turning from the sink where she was scrubbing potatoes, 'When was the last time you were left on your own, may I ask?'

'Well, you never know, I live in fear of desertion,' replied the uncle, winking at Luke as he sat down in an armchair by the range. 'You're always threatening to take off just to see how we'd manage,' he added.

Luke's aunt wiped her hands on a tea towel and filled a saucepan with cold water, and Luke saw that she was smiling to herself.

'Two days,' she said, turning with the saucepan. 'I'd give them two days before catastrophe hit the place...'

Luke was thinking about Rosie, but before he could say anything his uncle spoke, changing the subject, 'Oh and Maura, that fence is down again,' he said, 'and the Friesian is gone through to McIntyre's. Remind me to fix it up properly.'

His uncle rattled on, listing more jobs to be done the next day, but Luke didn't hear anymore. He was wondering where Rosie could be. His daydream was interrupted when he heard his name spoken.

'Luke can do it,' his aunt was saying, 'can't you, Luke?'

Luke snapped back to the kitchen: 'Sorry, Maura, what were you saying,' he asked.

'You can walk over to McIntyre's tomorrow and pick up the Friesian, can't you?'

'Seeing as yourself and herself are best friends and all of that, nearly inseparable,' said a voice behind him.

Luke turned to face the speaker, his cousin, Thomas, who had just come into the kitchen.

Thomas had brown curly hair and smiley eyes, and Luke wasn't really sure if he liked him. He was easy-going and polite like his father, but often with an edge of sarcasm that Luke detected and disliked.

'How do you mean, Thomas,' asked his father.

'Well, isn't he down there every evening since he got here hugging and patting that oul' cow?'

Luke felt redness starting in his neck and flame onto his cheeks. He wanted to say something, but the words were a hundred miles away in the bottom of his stomach.

The three people in the room with him were like dummies in a shop window; unmoving, his aunt at the range, his uncle in the armchair, the cousin with the curly hair looking at him, eyebrows raised in mockery.

'Well, Luke's the man for the job, so ,' his uncle said, after a pause. 'Now Luke, will ye throw on that kettle there and make us a cup of tea,' continued the uncle, and the moment was forgotten by all of them, except Luke.

Luke was downstairs very early next morning. The summer light slanted into the kitchen from the east, painting silvered yellow shafts of brightness in unfamiliar places.

Luke sat at the table, a long scratched wooden one, and watched the shadows in the kitchen, fascinated, while the morning quietly grew around him. He wondered how he was supposed to retrieve Rosie from the neighbouring herd of sixty Friesians, all black and white, all with mournful eyes and long lashes.

'Luke can do it,' they had said, the words final in the kitchen, the same kitchen where he now sat. Then it had been full of family, the conversation flitting, skipping, changing tone and content as the doings of the day were dissected or dismissed. Luke had missed most of it, drowning slowly in the casual challenge of retrieving Rosie.

Would they tell him how to go about it? Could he ask? Could he dare ask or would the question amuse, then flow along, unanswered, in the current of conversation? Luke did not want to fail, though he knew Thomas wanted him to. To fail and in so doing to provide the silent evidence that Luke was an idiot from the city, sentimental about farm animals, unable to handle them. All this to provide himself with an unspoken superiority.

Luke looked at the kitchen clock - 5.45. He had slept badly, tossing anxiously in his bed, and the first birdsong at the edge of the day had woken him fully. He sat there for what seemed a long time, wondering what to do until the silence of early morning had evaporated with the dew, and the secret shadows had merged into more familiar ones. Everything he had ever learned about life in his ten short years rolled around in his head, all mixed up together, and he felt very young.

'Always mark your man.' Who was his man? Was it Rosie or his sly cousin?' Always do your best and things will turn out fine.' He would do his best if only he knew what to do. 'Ask your guardian angel for help.' He did that.

'What can you do to help yourself here?' He had the answer to that one. Slowly he rose, got a sheet of paper and a black marker from a drawer in the kitchen and began to draw a cow. Closing his eyes, Luke tried to recall every detail of Rosie's markings. Was she a white cow with black markings or a black cow with white markings? Slowly, the drawing took shape. Fifteen minutes and several rub-outs later, he had a good impression of a Friesian.

Engrossed, he didn't hear the soft footsteps behind him come to a halt at his shoulder.

'That's very good Luke, you take that from the other side of the family don't you?' His aunt, in a fluffy dressing gown, was staring over his shoulder at the drawing.

Luke urgently wanted to hide the drawing before she read his desperation on the page, but it was too late.

Ignoring, or unaware of Luke's discomfort, his aunt held the page up to eye level, studied it and said: 'Great job Luke. If that doesn't take a first in the art section of the agricultural show, Grandma's a Dutchman. Now, will you have a bite of breakfast with me before these other hooligans get up?'

Later that morning Luke walked toward the cowshed, past Thomas, his lips pursed in the kind of whistle that makes no sound at all.

'Going to McIntyre's now, are ye? Well, don't come back empty-handed anyway.' The jeer in Thomas's voice was unmistakable.

Luke took a breath the way they told you in Gaelic training, to steady yourself and focus, and stood straight, feet on the ground, the way his Dad had told him to stand that time he had been bullied in third class.

He counted to ten before replying, and when he did the words came out of nowhere, softly: 'Sure, come on with me if you want to see how it's done.' Then he picked up a coiled rope and set off down the road, ten years old and resolute, his hopes and wishes pinned to a drawing of a cow.

McIntyre's was about a half mile away, down a sort of track that led between the two farms of land. Sunlight danced through green summer leaves and the Irish countryside was at its best. Luke considered his options. He could sift through the sixty plus Friesian herd and using his drawing and memory, select the cow that looked most like Rosie, hoping it WAS Rosie. Or, he could stand in the middle of the herd and call her name, though the thoughts of that left his blood cold, especially if his cousin ever got to hear of it.

The closer he came to McIntyre's, the more the morning filled with dread. What if he couldn't find her?

Eddie McIntyre met him in the yard, a thin, red-haired man with bright blue eyes. He put down the creamery can he was carrying and listened gravely to Luke. Then they walked together to the field where the straying Rosie stood somewhere among her own kind, a herd of black and white Friesians, all the same, none exactly alike, all beautiful. Luke had butterflies in his stomach.

Eddie opened the gate and Luke was suddenly among the herd, black and white everywhere. His legs wouldn't move. At all. 'Walk to the top of the field, Luke, I'll wait here.'

Then, of course, his legs did move, and Luke walked through the cows, through the pairs of great calm eyes, the chewing cuds, the warm smell of cow, the gently swishing tails. 'The Sligo colours,' he thought to himself, 'black and white,' and he felt a tickle of laughter rise in his stomach.

Smiling at his own joke, he reached the top of the field, free from the black and white tapestry of the animals. Standing there in the sunlight, wondering what to do next, he noticed a stirring in the herd, a movement not consistent with its lazy grazing, and realised that a single cow was making her way through it towards him, to the top of the field. In an instant he recognised her, and his small body sagged in relief.

When she reached Luke, he put his arms around her neck and called her a silly girl. Eddie McIntyre, watching at the gate, smiled to himself.

'You knew me, you knew me,' Luke whispered in Rosie's ear and she nudged him gently like a huge soft dog. 'Oh thanks, Rosie, you lamb!'

The other cows stared for a moment, then went back to plucking the grass in easy mouthfuls. Luke slipped the rope around the cow's neck, still talking to her, and together they walked towards Eddie McIntyre, nodding his head by the gate.

'Aren't you the cheeky madam,' he said to Rosie, 'putting young Luke here to all this bother. Good thing you have a way with cows,' he added, looking at Luke and still nodding.

Still smiling and feeling two foot taller, Luke led Rosie home through the sunlight and the hedgerows, and walked through the gateposts of his uncle's farm: Caesar returned with the great and precious prize that would make him a hero in the eyes of all who saw him. At least for the rest of that Summer.

Pig Tales

A memory by **Paddy Reid**
Balbriggan, Co. Dublin

In the mid 1960s laws were brought in forbidding piggeries in the city, and my uncle had to keep the pigs out in Fingal.

For several years until the early 1960s I had the less than glamorous job of collecting pig swill from Moore Street in Dublin. This was done for an uncle who kept a piggery in Dublin's inner city. Six weeks or so before the pigs were to be sold, they would be brought in from the Fingal area to be fattened up.

My uncle paid poorly for my work, a shilling a week each was all I could expect. Anyone looking at him chewing on his briar pipe, bale twine holding his shabby overcoat together, might be tempted to give him back his shilling out of pity, if one didn't know him.

To get me started, he supplied a long-handled box-cart that was to be loaded to the brim (nothing less would do) from the discarded fruit and vegetables dumped in Moore Street at the end of each working day.

As the stallholders' work-day ended, so mine would begin. I had to time the collection just right. There was less than an hour between the sellers packing up for the day, and the bin collectors from Dublin Corporation clearing everything disposable from the street.

I collected apples, tomatoes, pears, plums, carrots, potatoes, turnips, cabbages and cauliflower among others. Never citrus fruits such as oranges or lemons, as these 'didn't agree' with the pigs.

When fully loaded, the box-car was very hard to pull. Its wooden sides were bloated out, juices pouring out from gaps in the timber frame. I soon learned that it was too much work and asked one of my younger brothers to help. That meant sharing the measly money with him.

At first we used a box-cart with pram wheels. This was fast indeed, but the wheels soon collapsed when it was fully loaded. The cart was then fitted with steel balL-bearing wheels, making it slower but taking the load better. Once full, we tried to set a decent pace lest it would stall on the rough city roads.

This meant not stopping for such trivial things as traffic lights as this would slow us too much. Once stopped, it was a real drag to get going again. Behind us we left a trail of ripe-smelling liquid as the box-car leaked like a sieve, especially from a load of over-ripe soft produce like tomatoes.

We charged out at full tilt toward town, metal wheels banging on the cobblestones. Passing under the railway bridge in Seville Place, the rattling noise echoed off the archway walls like a demented Tommy gun.

When a large herd of cattle being driven from the market on the North Circular Road to the cattle boats was passing nearby, cows panicked at the noise and instantly began to scatter. We ran behind a concrete pillar to avoid the stampede. One cow tore back up Portland Row and impaled itself on a garden railing. I can still smell the fear and blood. A local butcher came running and put the animal out of its misery.

The box-car had been trampled to firewood. We trudged back to my uncle's yard and told him our tale.

'Thousands of them ran wild,' I said. He didn't say anything, just gave me a long, hard look. No money was to be had that day.

After that, we had to 'steer' clear whenever cattle were passing.

On rare occasions in Moore Street we would find a full tray of perfectly good fruit, usually apples, under a pile of cardboard or other rubbish, somehow left aside and forgotten by the stallholder. On these days we would put some aside for ourselves, then make a short detour to our home in the Diamond and leave the goodies to be devoured by a houseful of six hungry boys.

One wet wintry evening, I passed by Conway's Pub in Parnell Street, opposite the Rotunda Hospital.

A man called out from the pub doorway.

'Any good apples,' he asked, smiling. 'You look like a drowned rat.'

I was soaked. I dug into the cart, pulling out a good apple, rubbed it dry on my sleeve and handed it to him without a word.

He dug into his coat pocket and pulled out a two-shilling coin.

'That's too much,' I said, having no change on me.

'That's okay, son.' He ruffled my wet hair. 'I'll see you next time.'

He never did. Soon after, I saw his obituary photo in a newspaper. It gave his name as Brendan Behan and said he was a writer.

Later, it was fondly said of Brendan that he could never pass a pub or a beggar. I must have resembled the latter on that long-ago day.

To add to our meagre slop earnings, we also sold Sunday newspapers on Saturday evenings. Our best sales were at the huge side door of the GPO that housed Radio Eireann. People such as Frankie Byrne, Terry Wogan and other then relatively unknown radio DJs would quickly snap up lots of our papers. The rest we would sell in pubs such as Molloy's in Talbot Street and Madigan's in North Earl Street. If it was a very slow night, we'd run down as far as Clare's pub in Foley Street.

Clare's could be relied upon to have a man-sized brawl outside its doors late on Saturday nights, and we'd quickly sell our papers to the 'fight night' crowd of onlookers. Best of all was on days of an international rugby match, when we could sell all our papers within an hour, showing a profit of ten shillings -.a small fortune and more fun than pig slops.

Back then, Moore Street often smelled of something else, an abattoir on Moore Lane that stank to high heaven on warm summer days. Once, out of curiosity, I went to peek at the scene. I was taken aback by the amount of blood in the yard, the loud buzzing made by clouds of bluebottles, and the fear I saw in the cows' eyes.

In the mid 1960s, Dublin Corporation brought in hygiene bye-laws and the slaughterhouse was relocated. Laws were also brought in to forbid piggeries in the city. My uncle had to keep the pigs out in Fingal.

By then, I had retired from slop-collecting to get a 'real' job as a messenger boy. Pulling box-cars was good practice for pushing a big old messenger bike around the city, but my feet could not reach both bike pedals. I had pretended that I could ride a bike, instead I scooted along on one pedal until I 'grew' into the job.

But that, as they say, is a sceal eile (another story).

NEVER TOO LATE

By JANET FARRELL
Ballycarney, Carlow

Liz's eye fell on the man speaking to the cashier. There was
something familiar about him. Surely he couldn't be.....

The meeting having finally finished, the boardroom
quickly began to empty. Tom tidied up his papers and
made his way back to his office. Back at his desk, Tom
sat at his computer. It was a reasonably big office as befitted
Tom's position as Financial Controller of a Dublin city centre
hospital. Situated on the top floor, it gave him commanding
views of the city. Glancing out the window, Tom noticed a gust
of autumnal wind blow some leaves down to the russet carpet
below

Having responded to the urgent emails, Tom's mind came
back to the meeting that afternoon. It was the latest in a series
of meetings concerning the hospital's voluntary redundancy
scheme. As Financial Controller, he had an obvious interest
in it, but he was thinking of applying for the scheme himself.
Would it be a good idea to take it?

He had been working at the hospital for 40 years, rising
through the grades to Financial Controller. He would certainly
be eligible, but would it be a good idea for him to take it? He
considered his life as it stood at the moment. His health was
good; he had looked after himself through the years, kept fit.
He had his own house in a quiet cul-de-sac, just a bus ride
away from the city centre. Never married; he wouldn't have to
consider the impact of redundancy on a wife or family.

Sometimes it was hard to believe forty years had passed since
he had come to Dublin from 'down the country' as the Dubs
would say. He loved living in Dublin, always something to
do, always somewhere to go. He had made good friends here
through work, and with his interest in GAA through the years.

Maybe if he took the redundancy, he might move back home . . . or maybe not. He didn't like to think of the circumstances of his coming to Dublin, though time had eased the hurt. He wondered what Liz was doing now. Liz! He hadn't thought about her for a long time. Shutting down the computer, Tom got ready to leave the office, work over for the day.

Closing her front door with one hand, and carrying her shopping bag in the other, Liz walked through to the kitchen. She had only bought a few essentials in the little shop beside the school where she worked. The rest could wait until she did a big shop on Saturday. Not that she needed to buy much nowadays. Emma her youngest, had just started college in Dublin and her two sons were working, one in Dublin and one in London. She took off her coat and hung it up on the hallstand, her hand brushing against her husband's old raincoat as she did so.

Glad to be home after a day's teaching, Liz began putting away her shopping. She loved this house with its views of the countryside and surrounding hills. It reminded her of her childhood home on the farm. The gardens that surrounded were planned and designed by her husband and were his pride and joy.

She especially loved the view from the kitchen where she could see the seasons change, and she often found the stresses of the day melt away as she sat looking out with a cup in tea in hand. As Liz went to fill the kettle, the phone rang.

Tom scanned the redundancy forms again and remembered those first days in Dublin. He was just twenty years old when he moved up. He had been working as a labourer for different farmers around home. There weren't too many alternatives then.

It was alright; but he and Liz had wanted to get married, and he knew they needed more than what a casual labourer's wages would get them. He had met Liz when he came to work on her parents' farm. She was seventeen and had just finished secondary school. She helped her mother preparing meals for the workmen, and sometimes worked outside, especially if there was help needed with the livestock.

They worked together throughout the summer and she was always friendly and willing to chat and they were soon firm friends. Before long, their friendship turned to something deeper, and they knew they wanted to get married.

Fearing Liz's parents mightn't approve of her marrying so young they made plans. Tom would move to Dublin and get a job, and find somewhere for them to live. He would send Liz his address, and once he was settled she could join him and they could get married in Dublin. Her parents were bound to accept the relationship then. Living in Dublin, it would be handy to go home at intervals to visit Tom's widowed mother on her smallholding.

So, full of dreams and enthusiasm, Tom arrived in Dublin. He wrote to Liz as soon as he found a flat. It was really only a bed-sit, but he meant to move somewhere bigger as soon as he got a job. It would be no problem finding a bigger place; the papers were always full of ads for flats. He was lucky to get a job as a porter in the hospital within a fortnight of arriving. He told all this to Liz in a letter too.

He wasn't too worried about not getting a reply from Liz yet. Everyone knew the post was unreliable, didn't they? Anyway, he trusted Liz would keep her word. He wrote to his mother too, though he didn't mention Liz. He decided it was better that all the parents be told at the same time. It would make the surprise more special. He continued writing to Liz.

After two months of no replies, his confidence began to waver. What had gone wrong? Surely, his mother would mention if Liz had married, or he dreaded the thought, was ill or dead. She always wrote of the news about the neighbours from home. After six months, he stopped writing. It was obvious Liz had changed her mind. And without telling him. That was what hurt the most.

By this stage, Tom, though enjoying his job as porter, knew he was capable of more. He began to take night classes, and was successful in getting a job as Clerical Officer. Continuing with the night classes, he studied accountancy and rose through the grades to Financial Controller where he was now.

Eight months after Tom moved to Dublin, Tom's mother died. Going home to the funeral, it was the first time he had been back. He heard Liz had gone to college, teacher training he thought.

He quickly learned to love Dublin. He frequently went to matches in Croke Park and Lansdowne Road. One of his favourite places was St Stephen's Green. A little piece of green countryside in the centre of the city. He never tired of going there no matter the season. Popular with his colleagues, he was friendly and good humoured, and he soon settled in.

He had to admit life had been good to him. Of course, there had been other girlfriends over the years, girls who worked in the office and sisters of friends, but they never lasted. None of them worked out for one reason or another. He wondered what Liz was doing now, how she was ... Tom sighed, put the forms away and went down to the canteen for some lunch.

Liz looked at Emma with amusement as she rapidly typed away on her mobile phone, as she lay in the hospital bed. The operation had gone well, and Emma, though a bit pale, seemed in good form.

'I think I'll get a sandwich. I think I noticed a canteen downstairs when I came in,' Liz said finally.

Emma didn't look up. 'OK, I've already had something. I'll be fine for a while on my own. I'll be going on Facebook next. Let everyone know how I survived appendicitis!'

'Right,' Liz said, 'I won't be long'. It had been a tiring couple of days since she had received the phone call to say that Emma was being sent to hospital with stomach pains. Appendicitis, the doctors said and Emma had had surgery last night. Emma was her youngest child in her first year of college in UCD.

Paying for her chicken sandwich and tea, Liz sat at the nearest table to the cash register in the hospital canteen. From here, Liz could see the customers lining up to pay for their food. It was almost 1.30 and the small canteen was beginning to fill up.

Watching the queue approach the cash register, Liz's eye fell on the man speaking to the cashier. He looked so familiar, surely he couldn't be ... But even though so many years had passed since she had last seen him, she knew immediately who it was.

Sensing he was being watched, Tom turned from the cashier and looked at the woman who was sitting at the nearby table. Holding her teacup in mid air, she was watching him with a look of sudden recognition on her face. Even though it had been so long since he had seen her last, he would have known her anywhere.

Leaving his tray behind, he walked towards her. 'Liz?' he said, 'Yes, Tom! My God, I can't believe it..... after all these years, do you work here?' she babbled.

'Yes' he said shortly, 'I've worked here since I came to Dublin. Of course I told you a long time ago in the letters. Why did you never reply?' he couldn't help asking.

'I never got them,' she replied quietly.

'What? Never got them? Surely the postal service can't be that bad!' he said, his voice rising slightly.

'It wasn't the Post Office!' she interrupted, 'it was my mother. She met the postman when your first letter came and opened it. I never saw it. After that she made sure to meet the postman to get every letter. She destroyed them all. I never knew.'

Tom remained silent as the full impact of what she said hit home. Tom sat down at the table and the story soon came out. How Liz's mother opened Liz's post without her knowing, because she felt she had a right to know who was writing to her daughter. How she never told Liz anything about it until years later. By then Liz had left college, found a teaching job and married another teacher at the school where she worked. She'd even had her children by then, her two sons and daughter Emma.

'Don't think too badly of her. It was a terrible thing she did. I think she just didn't want me moving to Dublin, you know with me being an only daughter, and Dublin seemed so far away then.'

Liz explained that Emma was a patient in the surgical ward. 'And your husband?' Tom asked, 'Is he here too?'

'No,' Liz replied. 'He died five years ago – cancer.'

'I'm sorry to hear that. I never got married myself,' he said.

There was silence for a few seconds. Liz continued: 'Of course, I thought you'd changed your mind at the time. I was so angry. But I started college and just got on with life. What else could I do? It must have been the same for you.'

'Yes,' he said simply.

Liz looked down at her cup and Tom was filled with a sense of warmth and affection for her. 'Look,' he said, 'If you like, we could meet again later. Have a proper conversation. When you're sure Emma is OK.'

Liz considered this, as the sun began to shine though the windows. 'Yes,' she said, 'I'd like that.'

THE STREET CLEANER

A MEMORY BY LIAM MULVIN
Truro, Cornwall

*He wore his old clothes with a pride I couldn't conceive of.
The years had bent him in half, yet he walked taller than
any man I knew.*

I never knew his name, but I can still see him after all these years. The lady in the tatty shop on the corner once told someone it was his birthday and he was seventy-two. I was shoplifting in the corner and was listening out carefully, so heard what she said.

He was an old man who must have fought in both world wars. I guessed he had seen much death and suffering, but he was just an old man, so I ignored him. People said he was quiet and decent. I had no connection with him at all.

I was sixty years younger than him almost to the day. I fought a war every day against my parents and against my school. I fought every bit of authority going. I had seen death, too, and witnessed suffering and I couldn't ignore that. I still saw no connection with him, and people said I was mouthy and a pest.

Three years passed and for all the years I went to that school I saw him nearly every day. I would walk out of my house and down the long hill to the lower main road. Reaching the crossroads, I would turn left and arrive at my school. Houses were everywhere, and his was halfway down the hill on the left.

I wore my school uniform carelessly and without pride. I carried a bag with school work inside that had been dashed off to the absolute minimum. My future was in that bag and I was throwing it away. The lump in my chest that should have been a heart beat out its hatred with a frightening and red-hot coldness. I suffered in my own misery without expectation or hope. Most of all, I was angry; so angry, yet so afraid of it.

He wore his old clothes with a pride I couldn't conceive of. The years had bent him almost in half, yet he walked taller than any man I knew. Solid, dependable army boots on his feet that sparked sometimes if the hobnails scraped a flint; baggy old corduroy trousers kept up with a length of string; an old jacket that hung further down at the front on top of a vest, shirt, and waistcoat; the whole topped off with a disreputable cap.

In front of him he pushed a wheelbarrow containing some carrier bags; a stiff-bristled broom; a soft-bristled broom and a shovel. His future was in that barrow and he pushed it with dignity. He never said anything that I ever heard, but he coughed a lot. Permanently wedged onto his lower lip was a roll-up.

I wasted my days at school with a monotonous regularity. Interested in only history, reading and writing, most of my days seemed to involve vast amounts of boredom and futile rebellion.

That bent old man was always out there somewhere though. No matter the weather, he walked the local area and cleaned and swept every day. Just a dozen or so roads and avenues but you knew he had been by. He took everything home, the rubbish, the recycling, and what he called his 'findings' - fag butts mainly to break down into his roll-ups, but sometimes coins or, oh I don't know, things I suppose.

It amused me sometimes to throw rubbish on the pavement for him. I didn't care because I knew he'd clear it up. In my mind, he was a reject and a waste of space, dirty old man, always grubby, always coughing, old humpy back. What a loser.

Then he wasn't there. Rubbish stayed on the road and in the gutters, cans were kicked along the pavements, but were still there in the evening. The streets looked unkempt and unloved. I would glance at his house, but it was all locked up and quiet. Someone mentioned pneumonia and mustard gas. Said he swore that the fags helped keep his chest clear.

He was back out on the streets about a month later. He looked pale, but still smiled a lot, smoked a lot, coughed a lot, and swept a lot. I ignored him as usual because he was old and I wasn't. Then one day it happened.

I was on my way home; alone, bitter, angry and late. Another detention behind me, and another day of deep, twisted rage and hurt, including a backside sore from another caning, was not helping my mood. Rounding the corner there was the old street cleaner and his barrow, and, without a thought, I threw my drinks can at him.

I stopped and watched the can spin towards him, liquid splashing out of the side. It missed him and landed in the gutter where it foamed and splashed a small puddle onto the floor. He put the barrow down and turned towards me and stared. Then it happened; our eyes locked and we connected.

I stared deeply into the mirrors of his soul as he stared deeply into mine. I don't know what he saw in my eyes, but I know what I saw in his. I saw a lifetime of pain, despair, anger, hurt, struggle and loss. I also saw a lifetime of courage, defiance, pride, heroism, forgiveness and love.

Nothing was said, yet everything was. I saw the life behind the man; I saw the man behind the barrow; I saw the man. I swear I stumbled a step forward as his eyes pulled away and he bent down and picked up the can and put it into his barrow. He coughed once before picking the handles up and pushing the barrow along the pavement and away from me.

In one look that old man humbled me, yet showed me a better path than the one I was walking. I never forgot him or the dignified look in his eyes that day.

A couple of weeks later, we moved to a different part of town and I never saw him again. On the day before we moved, I walked down to school for the last time. I hunched past him and we ignored each other as normal, though I was now coming free of the anger.

I looked back and, as he turned around briefly, I dropped a paper bag into the gutter. Inside was a small pack of ready to roll tobacco and a couple of packets of Rizla papers. It had cost most of the money from my paper round to add to his 'findings.'

That evening going home was the last time I saw him. He straightened up as well as he could and drew deeply on the roll-up in his mouth before smiling and nodding once at me. I nodded back and watched as he picked up the barrow and wheeled it off down the road.

I still see him after all these years. He stares back at me from my shaving mirror...

SKIPPING TIME

By JOHN MARTIN
Kilcullen, Co. Kildare

On the surface, Jim was a highly successful businessman, but in his heart he knew there was something missing from his life.

The engraving on the stone above the door of the two-classroom school proclaimed that it had been built in 1906. Now, fifty years later, the building still served the educational needs of the small rural village of Kilmore.

The pupils exploded into the early June sunshine eager to extract maximum value from the lunch hour. In the girls' playground the long skipping rope was produced. The girls surrounded the two selected to swing the rope. Ann Delaney, a tall girl with plaits flying, was called in. The assembly took up the chant to the rhythm of the skipping rope:

'Red,' skip, 'White,' skip, 'Blue,' skip, 'Yella,' skip - 'Who's,' skip, ' going,' skip, 'to be,' skip, 'your fella,' skip, ' J,' skip, 'J,' skip, 'I,' skip, 'I,' skip, 'M,' skip, 'M,' skip, 'Jim,' skip, 'Jim,' skip. Ann completed her turn with legs astride the rope, her face flushed from a combination of embarrassment and delight. The girls cheered and giggled.

On the other side of the long wall that separated the playgrounds, Jim Hogan also felt the heat rising in his cheeks. The chanting of the girls carried easily across the wall. The other boys were busy finishing their lunches and anticipating the rough and tumble of the football game to be played on the rocky surface of the playground. Piles of discarded jackets demarked the goal area. The crusts of jam sandwiches were thrown to the crows that had gathered in anticipation of the lunchtime scraps. Tom McGee sidled over to where Jim was sitting and punched him hard on the shoulder.

'D'ja hear that, Hogan, the girls think that you have a notion of Ann Delaney. I'd bet she's not on for it. I'd say she'd have better taste than that.'

Jim ignored the jibe and finished clearing up the scraps left over from his lunch. He supposed that he had a 'notion' regarding Ann, although he wasn't really clear what that meant. He enjoyed her company. He got to know her on the many occasions that they walked home from school over the years. She was bright and intelligent with a tomboy streak that was a bonus when they went exploring the old mill down at the river together or went searching for blackbirds nests in the hedges beside the railway line. Most of all she was fun to be with.

In a matter of minutes he was in the thick of the impromptu football match. Jim bade his time, and just as the school bell signalled that the game was coming to an end, he launched a full-blooded shoulder charge into the beefy Tom McGee. McGee hit the ground with a thud which knocked the wind from him. As he struggled to get his breath back, Jim leant over him, gave him his hand and whispered in his ear: 'You'd do well to keep your ideas about Ann Delaney to yourself.'

June drew to a close and the long summer holidays arrived at last. Jim Hogan did not return to Kilmore National School when it reopened in early September. Jim's father was the local Garda Sergeant and with the education of his only child uppermost in mind, he had requested a transfer to a town where secondary school facilities were available.

And so, in early July, the Hogan family departed Kilmore for the town of Lisbeg, located some fifty miles away. Jim knelt on the back seat and gathered his last views of Kilmore through the rear window of the hired car as it traversed the main and only street of the village from the Garda Station to the main road. Down they drove, past the Post office, McGees' public house and the blacksmiths' forge. A group of villagers had gathered outside the church to wave farewell to the popular family.

Further on, a knot of children placed themselves outside the gates of the school in order to gain a better view. Jim's gaze was drawn to the figure of Ann Delaney who detached herself from the group and ran down the street after the departing car. Her plaits flew in the wind and she waved wildly with both hands. Jim raised his hand and returned the wave. As he did so, he experienced a feeling in his stomach that he had never felt before.

Jim had no occasion to return to Kilmore in the years that followed. A successful run through the secondary school system rewarded him with a place at university from where he graduated with a first class honours degree in engineering.

Over the next four decades, Jim combined his professional skills with a wanderlust that took him all over the Middle East and farther afield to Australia.

During the years before her death, Jim's mother fervently prayed that her only son would return to Ireland, meet a nice girl and settle down to a domesticated existence which would provide her with the grandchildren she craved. However her prayers were not answered and Jim's return to his homeland did not occur until the mid 1990s, long after both of his parents had gone to their eternal rewards.

During his stints in the Middle East and beyond, Jim had devoted himself to his work and had found little time for social contacts. On his return to Ireland, he set up his own engineering company in Dublin and found that his international experience stood him in good stead in establishing himself in business. On the surface he was the epitome of a successful businessman. Financially secure, he purchased a house in the suburbs but found it difficult to cope with the loneliness of the empty rooms. He felt in his heart that something was missing from his life.

With time on his hands at weekends, Jim took to touring around the country, staying in different locations and exploring the local heritage and historical sites. On his way back from one of his outings he passed a signpost for Lisbeg and, on a sudden impulse, he diverted from his route and found himself devoting the afternoon to revisiting the scenes of his teenage days.

Few of his secondary school pals still lived in the area. Enquiries elicited that most of them had emigrated during the harsh times of the 1980s. Late in the evening, realising that he was hungry and facing the long journey home, he decided to treat himself to dinner in the Commercial Hotel. His memories of the hotel centered on the special occasions that his parents had taken him there to celebrate family occasions. The dining room had changed little in the forty years since he had last frequented it on the night before he set out on the first of his many overseas journeys.

The food was excellent and the Polish waitress attentive and pleasant. Jim had just finished his main course when a tapping sound caught his attention. The rhythm was familiar but he could not place where he had heard it before. Turning in his chair, he saw that the woman seated on her own at a table near the window was tapping on the table with the handle of a spoon.

There was something about her which seemed familiar, but he just couldn't place where he had seen her before. The woman returned his gaze and smiled. She resumed her tapping and this time she added the words.

'Red, White, Blue, Yella, Who is going to be your fella?'

An image flashed through Jim's mind, the schoolyard, the girls' playground, the skipping rope and the tall girl with the plaits. He rose from his chair and approached her table. The light in the dining room was dim, but strip off forty years, smooth out the creases and there she was!

'It can't be! Ann, Ann Delaney?'

'Where on earth did you drop out of, Jim Moran? You took your time recognising me.' Ann laughed.

'It's the plaits,' Jim responded, 'I miss the plaits!'

The Polish waitress, sensing the rapport between the couple, brought a chair to the table for Jim and produced a pot of coffee and two cups. An hour and a half later, the couple stood up and resumed their conversation in the lounge.

Their sharing of their stories revealed that Ann had gone to England to train as a nurse and had worked in a hospital in Manchester for six years. She was forced to return to Kilmore on the death of her mother in order to look after her father as her only brother had emigrated to Australia where he had married and established a new life for himself and his family.

She had devoted twenty years to caring for her father, and when he passed away she had applied for the position as district nurse in Lisbeg. She had quickly settled down in her new environment. She had sold the home in Kilmore and had bought and refurbished a neat cottage on the outskirts of Lisbeg where she now lived alone. It was well after midnight when Jim finally arrived home, armed with awoken memories and Ann's telephone number.

The chance encounter ignited a friendship which developed and intensified over the following months. Jim spent more and more time visiting Lisbeg to be with Ann, and one of their favourite destinations on their outings was the village of Kilmore which held such happy memories for both of them.

They visited the old mill, now a complete ruin; retraced their steps to the long vanished railway line, and inspected what remained of the once bustling two-roomed school.

It came as no surprise that twelve months after the meeting in the Commercial Hotel, Ann and Jim decided to have their wedding celebrated in St Patrick's Church in Kilmore where they had approached the altar together on the day of their First Communion many years before.

The village was abuzz with excitement on the morning of the wedding. The church was filled with well-wishers who had fond memories of the pair when they had been children.

As the happy couple emerged from the Church door, a surprise awaited them. Tom McGee, who had inherited the local pub from his uncle, had a word with Miss Evans, the recently appointed principal of the new Kilmore National School, and so, as the newly-marrieds took their first steps towards their future, they were transported to the past. The girls from sixth class had set up in the church grounds. Under tutelage from Tom McGee they had prepared a skipping session. The rope twirled and the assembly took up the chant. A tall girl with plaits hanging down her back took her turn as the girls called out in unison:

'Red,' skip, ' White,' skip, ' Blue,' skip, 'Yella,' skip – 'Who's,' skip, ' going,' skip, 'to be,' skip, ' your fella,' skip, ' J,' skip, 'J,' skip, 'I,' skip, 'I,' skip, 'M,' skip, 'M,' skip, 'Jim' skip, ' Jim' skip.

The school children cheered and danced with delight. Jim held Ann's hand tightly as the tears welled in her eyes.

Tom McGee was the first to rush forward to wish the couple well. He planted a kiss on Ann's cheek, punched Jim on the shoulder, took him firmly by the hand and whispered in his ear: 'Looks like she had good taste after all – eventually!'

WILD FLOWERS

By KATHLEEN CURTIN

Neully-sur-Seine, France

Coming back was the most difficult part for Paula, but she felt she could find the answers to many questions in Rathdoon.

It was just a farm-yard, but my two children stood there defenceless. I rested my hand on the iron gate. I could see what they saw - fields, the steep hill sloping down the valley to the river, cows grazing or lying in the distance. In another paddock, a few ponies stood serenely.

But Greg and Zoe didn't move; they remained frozen on the spot, like deer dazzled by bright lights. They were stripped of everything that flashed, beeped and buzzed. They didn't know what to do. Their hands twitched without phones and consoles to grasp. There were no buttons or controls to guide them. They weren't viewing the scene on a screen. This was real. Something caught in my throat.

I saw sympathy in the eyes of the man standing nearby. He said just to call him plain Tom. He wasn't a plain man; there was depth in those eyes that held an ocean of secrets. A vague recollection flickered in my mind, I dug deep in my buried memories, but it didn't come back to me. I told him to call me Paula.

'Can you make a living out of it, I mean - times are hard for farmers these days?' I asked a safe question.

He took it seriously. 'Times have never been easy. I can't say if I make a lot of money from it, but I wouldn't know what else to do. I earn enough from the cows to live on, and to allow me to indulge in my ponies. It's my pleasure to give children riding lessons.'

'It's kind of you, Tom, to show us round your farm, and give my kids time to decide.' I meant it. I'd struggled to get them to come this far. It had taken lots of cajoling and persuading to prise them away from their online social lives. When faced with cranky outbursts, I'd threatened to cut their pocket money. That had swung it. In another year or so, that trick would no longer work.

'I haven't shown you anything yet,' he smiled. 'They have been on a farm before, haven't they, they have been to the countryside?'

Not really, I thought. 'Sort of,' I said, 'but I hope they're going to discover a lot more of country life in the future. We only moved last week. Our flat is just outside Rathdoon, we are practically next door to fields and nature.'

'Next door,' he seemed to think about that; 'whether we live in the town or the city, we're all in the middle of nature, one way or another.'

'Put like that, you're right. Anyway, it will be good for Greg and Zoe to take riding lessons.'

He studied me more closely, 'I remember you, Paula.'

'Do you?'

'You're a few years younger than me, but, yes, I remember you, Pauline O'Connor. It's a small world and Rathdoon town and parish aren't exactly big places.'

I tried to situate him and couldn't. A few years is a lot when you're very young. I hadn't mixed with many locally. I'd been packed off to boarding school as soon as my parents had seen my wandering eye. That hadn't stopped me though. If anything, boarding school had reinforced my desire to break away. But, it had also cut me off from my friends and weakened my roots at home. I'd suffered from that. Now, I'd returned and I felt like a stranger.

'I was in a hurry back then, anxious to get out, get going and see the world.'

'And did you?' he inquired.

'Did I what?'

'See the world?'

'Some of it, yes. I travelled a lot before getting tied down, as they say. Then I learnt about life. I don't regret it.'

He opened the gate, winked at Greg and Zoe. 'I know what I'd do if I was standing in front of a treasure, I'd enjoy it.'

They looked at him dumbly, not a word came out of their mouths.

Were my lot worse than any other teenagers? I'd tried to be strong and to go it alone. I thought I'd been managing okay. I wasn't the perfect role model, but not that bad. I saw the hunched shoulders of Zoe. I knew her, she was my own daughter, but I'd never seen her like that. Greg, one year younger, wasn't any better. He stood pale faced. His eyes, that should have been bright, were dulled from indoor living. He bore all the marks of hours sitting in front of displays and monitors.

They stood at the threshold of wide, open countryside, like two creatures that had spent their lives cooped up in a cage. You opened the door and they didn't want to fly out. His offer of freedom was met with bewilderment. They could navigate through the vastness of cyberspace, and yet, they couldn't dive in to those lush, green fields.

'Come,' Tom insisted, 'come with me, don't be afraid, the ground is dry.'

He led us through the first field; it was comforting and soothing. To my relief, the children gradually defrosted and began to take in their surroundings. They started moving more freely, quickening their pace, edging their way out of ear shot so that they could whisper together, while still keeping me in their sights.

He turned to me. 'Was it hard coming back?'

'I don't know that yet. But so far, it's not as bad as I expected. The most difficult part was taking the decision to return. Now that I'm here, I'm determined to make it work. I don't have the hunger or wanderlust that I used to have. I guess you'd call that calming down, getting sense. I think I can find the answers to many questions here. I suppose I'm getting older and wiser.'

'Oh, I don't know,' he said, 'we have to keep that grain of folly. We shouldn't let the embers die out.'

I lifted my eyes to his, in time to see the humour there. 'And you, did you want to leave, go somewhere else?'

'No,' he said, 'I like my hills. I've travelled, who hasn't, for holidays and short trips. But, I always want to come back here. I've relatives and good neighbours who are able to take over running the farm for those periods. I'm lucky to have people like that around me. Anyway, a week or ten days is as long as I can, or would, ever want to go away for.'

Greg and Zoe had reached the river. We hurried to catch up with them.

I stumbled, he took my arm lightly. 'Careful.'

'Thanks.'

'Are you all right in the flat, do you have enough space?' he asked.

'Yes.'

It was a small flat in the outskirts of town. I'd picked up a job at the big supermarket. That would help until I got my bearings.

The children were eying the cows suspiciously. Finally, Tom called to them and they came running back excitedly.

'Can we try the ponies now,' asked Greg, 'and can we go fishing in the river?'

'Yes,' chorused Zoe, 'please, please.'

Tom nodded, 'I was only waiting for you to ask, but let's deal with the ponies first.'

It didn't take long before I heard their shrieks of joy as they were carried on pony back. Tom supervised closely. 'If you're going to learn to ride properly, you'll have to come every week and you'll have to work hard, to groom and feed them, too. That's part of the deal. Greg, Zoe, do you agree to that?'

They gave a resounding 'yes.' I could feel that they really meant it.

Tom must have read something in my face. 'If you came back for answers, then I think you have at least one answer.'

'I do, Rathdoon is my home and will be home also for my children.'

'That's right,' he agreed.

Home, I thought, this was home. 'Yes, we all come from somewhere and the kids need to know that. No matter what we think, we aren't rootless tumbleweed, blowing in the wind.'

He laughed, it changed his face. 'You're quite the philosopher. But I agree, everybody and everything has a home.' He looked at me. 'Wild flowers, too.'

I looked away.

I recalled that night; it came back to me like a dream. How our minds teased us, and how easily our memories played hide and seek, selecting what to filter in or out. I saw it again; the bright disco lights, a tall boy asking me shyly to dance, and I refusing. A farmer's son didn't promise thrills. I'd eyes only for the motorbike gang. I felt now how my refusal must have hurt him, dented his confidence. I'd tossed it off. It was no big deal; guys asked you to dance, you said yes or no. It happened all the time. I'd been on a high, dancing the night away, showing off and daring everybody with my moves.

The disco had ended and, as always, people had hung around afterwards; getting chips and burgers, planning where to go next.

It had been a wet night and I'd had too much to drink. I'd staggered stupidly into a lane. A couple of guys had followed me down there. I hadn't realized the danger or their intention. But he had. He'd appeared at the top of the lane; it was enough to send them running away. How silly and careless I'd been back in those days. I couldn't even remember how I'd gotten home, but I suspect that he'd never left me out of his sight.

'Tom, I remember you now, how could I have forgotten.'

He waited - I continued: 'I was quite a flirt then. I didn't know it, I was testing all the limits, trying to find out who I was. I was just a young girl trying to grow up. Thank you for being my guardian that night.'

'I'm glad you came back, Paula.'

'Me, too.'

We looked at each other. There was hope and a promise. That was enough.

MAGICAL VISIT

A MEMORY BY TOM AHERNE

Carrigkerry, Co. Limerick

How a Christmas tradition brought joy to an elderly couple.

I well remember one of my earliest trips hunting the wren around West Limerick in the sixties and the warm welcome we received along our route. It was back in the era of walking - before transport became available, and I recall our visit to one household in particular on Christmas Night.

Our group totalled about a dozen, dressed in our traditional green, white and gold sashes, with white trousers, and peaked caps covered in the traditional way. We had a couple of accordions and fiddles, four bodhrans, and talented step-dancers and singers. The latter was a must to fill the hearts of the people with the music, song and dance they grew up with. Our captain and cashier carried the decorated holly bush bugle and money bag. Our flag with our name printed in bold letters, was carried by two more.

With the help of a poor torch, we marched in single file up the boreen, to the house in the distance, carefully avoiding the potholes and trying to stay on the path. The trees formed a guard of honour over us as the branches leaned inwards over the narrow boreen. Our hobnailed boots made loud noises on the icy slush and slippery leaves, as we spied the candle- lit windows of the old whitewashed house.

The sudden bark of a dog sounded like thunder on this cold and calm night, and grew louder as we approached and could smell the aroma of the peat smoke from the chimney. We started up 'O'Rahilly's March' as we made our way through the narrow gate and up to the welcome light coming from the open door. We entered and made a circle around the wooden table that stood in the centre of the kitchen floor.

Our caps were nearly touching the oil lamp hanging from the centre rafter providing the light. The walls were newly whitewashed, with holly and laurel decorating the pictures and windows. Our Lady's picture hung on one side of the room, its frame yellow from the smoking fire, and the Sacred Heart in similar condition on the other side. The four chairs were covered in sugan rope and painted brown, and the kettle and pots, hanging from the crane over the open fire, were black with soot.

There were two corresponding clevy holes at each side of the fireplace. In one were the tea canister and other household utensils, and the other held the Holy Bible, Old Moore's Almanac, Rosary Beads and prayer books.

The man of the house wore a childish smile, as he pressed tobacco in the palm of his hand for his pipe. He kept time with our music with the heel of his foot that was covered with a darned stocking. The woman of the house stood with a walking stick in her hand and kept time with the music, by tapping on the paved floor, and she patted the dog with her other hand to stop his barking.

Our captain blew the bugle to finish the march and we were welcomed to their house and wished a very happy Christmas. This was followed by the usual request 'have ye any dancer?'

No sooner had the words left her mouth than the 'Boys of Bluehill' was belted out and we moved to give our dancer room to display the hornpipe steps. The tears filled the old couple's eyes as our dancer covered the floor. When the dance finished a low and slow hand-clap was heard from the old woman, to indicate it ended too quickly and could have gone on forever. The old man rose from his chair and took the pipe from his mouth, said 'a blast of a song would be nice' and he broke into 'Shanagolden' and placed the kettle on the fire.

Our singer duly obliged and the old woman, with one hand to her ear, listened with contentment. At the end of each verse the old couple would repeat such words as 'lovely', 'good on you' and 'fair play to you'. When finished the same lonesome clap of hands was heard and if the song had twenty verses, the same attention, interest and silence would have been observed.

When the song was over the tea was made, and Christmas cake, barm brack, and a dozen mugs were placed on the table.'Tisn't much we have to offer ye lads, but 'twill help ye along your road.' The tea and cake were received with great thanks, for our road was long and the night frosty. The bodhran players warmed their skins over the fire, the accordions were strapped on and the fiddles tuned up for a final blast of music.

Led by our captain, we departed in single file with the sound of 'O'Neill's March' in the old couple's ears. The three wise men brought gold, frankincense, and myrrh to the baby Jesus on Christmas night. We brought music, song, dance and laughter to this old couple, who in turn treated us to such hospitality. They followed us to the gate and bade us farewell as we marched away to the next house.

Memories

By Liam Donnelly
Stewartstown Park, Belfast

'Go back to sleep now,' she tells her husband. 'Follow your heart back to that lovely beach and all those wonderful memories. Walk with me once more in the moonlight.'

Bright morning sunshine streams through the casement window and spills across the floor onto the tartan rug that swathes my lower body. The vivid reds and greens fluoresce, projecting a dim picture onto the screen of the dormant television. But other more enticing pictures clamour for my attention in the garden beneath my window. Cape Daisies stand tall around the edge of a circular flower bed applauding the mixed Fuchsia that dance like ballerina in the glinting sunshine.

A miscellany of summer fragrance assails me through the narrow gap at the bottom of the window and lifts me up above the Cypress trees that skirt the edge of the lush gardens. I rise slowly into the blue sky and all at once I smell the salt air and there beneath me is the deeper blue of the Atlantic. The blue of the ocean is trimmed by a sweeping arc of white sand that disappears somewhere in the distance where the hazy purple hills recline in the stupor of summer heat.

I know this place well; I've been here before. It evokes warm memories of summers past but somehow the name eludes me. I am not perturbed for this is a day to be enjoyed, not a day for paltry concerns.

I'm on the sand now; beautiful white crystalline sand. I watch it sparkle in the sun as the superfine particles slip through my fingers. I grasp another fistful and watch and wonder as it drifts in the soft breeze blowing in from the shore. My eyes are drawn to the waters edge and the figure emerging from the water. I shade my eyes and strain to recognise the approaching figure, but it is still far off. I watch it shimmer and almost dissipate in the summer heat. Moving closer, the figure loses liquidity and takes on solid form. It is a woman gliding across the wet sand and now onto the dry white sand, her black swimsuit a harsh contrast.

I watch her with ever growing fascination. She is moving in my direction.

She looks slim and long of limb as she progresses up the beach. Her fluid movement has a kind of feline grace. She stops in front of me, just feet away. She raises both hands and smoothes her wet blonde hair back from her face. Water droplets gleam on every part of her body. Then, in a heart stopping moment she kneels down beside me and gives me the most beautiful smile I've ever seen.

'Aren't you getting into the water?' she asks, lying down at my side.

'Somebody has to look after the kids,' I say without even wondering or thinking that this situation is in any way odd. I hadn't noticed the kids earlier. I thought the beach was deserted, but now I can hear their voices. They are just twenty yards away playing in a sand pit. They've been there all the while, my seven years old daughter and my five years old son. I somehow know this and don't question it. Why should I? A man, his wife and children on a beach in high summer; what could be more natural?

I raise myself on one elbow and watch her as she dons sun shades and makes herself comfortable. The white sand clings to her wet limbs like golden sequins. I marvel at her beauty. Childbearing has left no discernible trace on her beautiful body. The sun plays on her smooth skin, deepening her natural tan. I feel an irresistible urge to kiss her, but she reads my mind and smiles behind her shades.

'The kids are watching,' she murmurs.

I smile, too, sensing promise, not reproach. I lean forward and kiss her anyway. Her lips are soft and yielding and as warm as the summer sun above us.

A door slams violently without warning and I am back in my room. So, too, is the old woman. The sight of her fills me with rage. I find myself cursing and swearing uncontrollably. Can no one take her back to her room? Where are the doctors and nurses? Why doesn't somebody do something?

She shouldn't be allowed to wander about the place annoying people. I came here to convalesce but I have no peace. She blights my every wakening hour with her interminable weeping. I try to reason with her. I ask her to leave me alone, but she doesn't understand my words. Is she deaf? I raise my voice but still there is no sign of understanding. She breaks off crying and launches into a garbled speech.

What? What the hell is she saying? I can't understand a damned word she is saying. Is she a foreign woman? Is that it? Or maybe she is out of her mind. Why doesn't someone take her in hand for her own safety and my sanity?

Outside my window the light is fading. Where has the day gone? The old woman is placid now; the weeping has stopped. Maybe if I pretend to sleep she will leave. Through half-closed eyelids I can see the huge white disc of the full moon rising up through the Cypress trees at the bottom of the twilit garden. I close my eyes and my breathing is steady and measured.

Gently the old woman takes my hand in hers. I mustn't flinch. I must show no sign of revulsion as she cradles my hand in her ancient gnarled hands. I must keep up the pretence of sleep until she leaves. She is speaking to me once again in her strange foreign tongue. It is unintelligible but her tone is soft and pleasant. The rise and fall of her voice has a gentle rhythm to it.

She caresses my hand and I find it strangely comforting. All my tensions melt away and I feel so relaxed. Each soothing word is like a pillow to rest upon. I float on a cloud of her soporific murmuring drifting off into the cool night and the full moon.

I am on the beach once more and the night is balmy. The tide is in and the full moon sits low on the horizon sending a river of pale yellow light flowing in to the shore. I am barefoot; so, too, is my wife. The sand retains some heat of the day; it tickles between my toes. We stand near the water's edge watching the moon rise, my arm around her waist and her arm around mine.

It is mid summer's night and the western horizon is as bright as day.

Along the beach a short distance away a shape morphs in the eerie light. It is a large Irish hare. It sits erect with long pointed ears sniffing the evening air. It regards us casually then melts away into the gloaming. My wife rests her head on my shoulder. Her golden blonde hair catches the moonlight. So too does her sleeveless white blouse. She raises her head and kisses me softly. I gaze into her chocolate-drop eyes and they too reflect the moonlight.

'Happy?' I ask.

'Yes,' she replies. 'But I still feel that ache. I don't know how I'll cope.'

'America won't be so bad. It'll be a great new life for the kids...and us too.'

'I know, I know, but I've been feeling so sentimental all day. This is probably the last time we will ever walk along this magic beach.'

'Is that a tear I see?'

'I can't help it. This is our very last time in Downings.'

'Downings!' I almost shout the word. 'Now I remember! Downings!'

'Downings!' the old woman repeats. Her heart leaps with sheer joy.

The sleeping form of her husband begins to stir, but she pours soothing words on him and gently caresses his old hands. She brushes the white hair from his forehead and tucks the tartan rug around him.

'Go back to sleep now. Follow your heart back to that lovely beach and all those lovely memories. Walk with me once more in the moonlight.' She smiles through her tears but these tears are tears of joy; joy that he had found some lovely memory to relive and some respite from the solitary confinement of his mind.

She had watched helplessly as Dementia took him into custody. Dementia was a harsh jailer; she knew there would be no parole or early release. She had watched his slow harrowing retreat into that dark realm from which there was no road back.

The disease had crept up on him like a thief in the night and invaded his mind. Quietly and insidiously it robbed him of reason. Slowly it siphoned off his intellect until there was nothing left but an empty husk.

When she looked into his vacant, unrecognising eyes she saw nothing. If the eyes are truly the windows of the soul then where was his soul? Had it left him for some secret limbo or was it manacled somewhere in the darkest recess of his mind. In the depths of her despair she had often wished him dead. Death was a merciful thing; there was bereavement, mourning and then healing. With Dementia there was no wake, with sympathy and reminiscence, no funeral to attend, no closure and no healing. But there was bereavement and mourning, day after day after day.

She could see no end to his long journey. She was physically and emotionally exhausted but she had never lost hope. She prayed that God would grant him refuge in the warmth of his fond memories. She prayed also for those random moments when some dormant neurotransmitter fired up and freed him from Dementia's grip. When he came back and tapped on the window of his soul, she would be there, waiting to greet him.

THE £5 NOTE

A memory by MAURA CONNOLLY
Naas, Co. Kildare

A valuable lesson is learned from a humiliating experience.

'And where is my £5.' I can still hear Molly Smith's piercing voice, as she demanded the £5. 'I gave you £10 and you gave me back the change from a fiver,' she said, as her usually calm, controlled demeanour changed to an almost hysterical, raging demonstration.

'But,' I said. 'No buts,' she retorted, 'give me back my proper change.'

'Mary, Mary, come out here. This young one should not be behind the counter. She cannot count. I don't know what they are teaching them in school these days.'

Mary, my boss, emerged from that little store behind the shop.

It was the summer I finished school and I was waiting for my starting date to commence my nursing career. I had a part-time job in the local shop in our quiet little village. I felt all grown up and sophisticated. Strangely, I do not remember how much I got paid or how I spent it. I was an adult at last, out in the world, and the honour and glory of working in a shop was enough for me.

Moreover, I had the chance to eye up the local boys and to hear all the gossip. Gossip was not tolerated in our home, and I can still hear my mother saying: 'If you cannot say something good about people, don't say it at all.'

I was now in the way of hearing all the juicy bits of village news. I recall wondering if the customers came in for the morning paper or was the shop a meeting place where neighbours exchanged the local news.

That paper was pushed into the bottom of the shopping bag to read later, while tales of local happenings were exchanged.

This was where the goings-on in the village took priority to national or international news.

Mary, or Mrs. Malone as I called her, came into the shop and, in her usual calm voice, asked: 'Well, what is the matter?' Molly's barrage could be heard by all as she repeated her side of to story and, of course, the shop was full of customers. I showed Mrs. Malone the money in the little box under the counter, explaining that the only £10 I had taken in that afternoon was from Mr. Hall. I remembered it so well, because he had only bought a box of matches, and I had to give him all the change, aware that I might be short of change before the shop closed. Molly continued to demand her money, stating that 'she was a loyal customer and what would that young one know anyway.'

Mrs. Malone went to the moneybox and handed Molly £5. I was devastated, embarrassed and did not know what to do or say. Molly took the money and left the shop as Mrs. Malone looked at me and said: 'I know you are in the right. Now there are customers waiting to be served.'

Molly became the bane of my life. She always asked for Mrs. Malone. If I had to serve her she counted out her change, stating in a loud, clear voice: 'You always have to check,' ensuring that everyone in the shop heard her.

My letter came and I started my new career. Before I left the shop, Mrs. Malone told me she knew it was difficult for me the day she took Molly's word over mine. She knew I was right, but added: 'Who knows what any one of us would be like if we had Molly's life. Sometimes we just have to let things go.'

I never did find out what Molly's life was like, but I did learn a lot that day. I learned about kindness, humility, caring about others and sometimes you have to let things go. It stood to me in my nursing life. I also learned that we do not know why people behave one way or another.

I forgot all about Molly, but not the lessons I learned from Mrs. Malone. Ironically, many years later, I had the privilege of sitting with Molly on the evening she died. A few days before that, I recognized her in her hospital bed. She knew me, too, and we chatted about our village, but never mentioned the shop.

Molly and I made our peace one evening when she looked up at me with a kindly face and told me: 'You were always a good girl.' We both knew what she meant. I sat with her and held her hand. She died later that evening.

SEE THE CHILD

By MAE LEONARD

Woodlands, Naas, Co. Kildare

'There's nothing wrong with the child,' her husband insisted, 'only too much molly-coddling. He needs to be outdoors more.'

Patricia's mouth goes dry with shock as she studies the drawing. Her heart does a sickening flip and she holds her breath as she stares at the picture again. It is perfect. A perfect copy of a section of the Harry Clarke stained-glass window they had seen the previous day at the Hugh Lane Gallery in Dublin. The image is clear and deftly executed in pencil.

'Is it my imagination,' she asks herself in an awed whisper and studies the picture once more. Yes, perfect. She wants to hug and kiss and slobber all over this little genius who is her son. She picks up the page from the kitchen table, but the child reaches out and grabs it and scrunches it with both his little hands. Then he tears it into bits and stuffs it all into his mouth. She anticipates what is coming next and quickly removes everything breakable from the table. His face turns red and he grits his teeth and he pounds the table with his fists. Bit by tiny bit, he spits out the chewed-up picture, and begins to scream until he is hoarse.

Finally, four-year-old Luke stops and stares at his mother defiantly. Patricia sighs. 'Fraught' is the word she uses when describing his attitude towards her, his moods and his lack of language.

The GP was somewhat vague in his diagnosis. Some form of autism, he had said, and referred her to a specialist in Dublin.

Patricia Maher was one of those women the years caught up on and left alone on the wrong side of thirty-five without a life's partner. Yet, she was a delightful person in company and a very competent nurse. Perhaps she was a bit too dedicated to her work. She even volunteered to help out at the local Day Centre for the Aged on her days off.

She had very little free time. Men found her off-putting. Maybe she looked a bit severe because she had inherited her father's aquiline nose on a little triangular face. Tall and thin, you couldn't exactly call her beautiful, but she had a pleasant smile, bright blue eyes and a head of luxuriant strawberry blonde hair that was usually pinned up tightly under her nurse's bonnet.

Declan Brennan opened his eyes after his operation and saw an angel. He thought he was in heaven. Those eyes followed every move, every crackle of Patricia's starched apron and every whiff of the lavender perfume she exuded. Having had an accident in work, whatever pain he felt from the fixing of his shattered leg came to nothing as she tended him in St. Joseph's Hospital. For the first time in his life he was in love.

And that life was a long, hard-working one. A truck driver, he never had time for the niceties of life. He worked morning, noon and night, and his haulage business thrived. Now, at fifty-two years of age, tucked into his hospital bed he felt like a giddy schoolboy. Patricia Maher had that kind of effect on him.

Patricia was aware of his interest in her and wasn't at all sure that she wanted it. A long-term relationship ended in tears after a betrayal. She felt she could never trust a man again. She had come to terms with her spinsterhood and was in the process of buying a house.

'Nurse!'

'Yes, Mr. Brennan.'

'Declan.'

'Yes, Declan. What can I do for you?'

'Marry me.'

Patricia laughed heartily before replying: 'And what would you do if I said yes?'

'I'd be the happiest man in the world.'

And out of that bit of hospital banter came a courtship in the true sense of the word. Declan battled with his injured leg with a determination that amazed her. He courted her the same way, providing constant, persistent attention that wore all her resistance down.

Six months later they were married. Declan was, indeed, the happiest man in the world. He put all his cards on the table for his new wife. He had very little education and even less experience of women. He knew he was no oil painting, but he was sincere and promised that he would cherish the girl he loved.

Patricia grew to appreciate his honesty and generosity and found it easy to love him back. Two years later they had a baby boy, and their joy was unconfined. Patricia came home from the Nursing Home with baby Luke to find a freshly-painted sign over the yard entrance:

DECLAN BRENNAN AND SON

The baby was fractious. He kept them awake with his persistent crying most nights. Patricia found him very difficult to soothe and she decided to give up any notion she had of going back to her job. She became a full-time mother to him, and Declan nodded in agreement. There was no need for her to work again as he earned a comfortable enough living for all of them.

Patricia had dreamt of a cuddlesome baby. She knitted jerseys of the softest powder-blue wool and bought only the best blankets and baby creams. Nothing was too much for this little man. Yet, even at a few weeks old, there was something in him that puzzled her. He wasn't the huggable baby that she expected.

As the months went by, Luke seemed to be getting more and more independent. She loved him to the point where her heart was bursting with the joy of him. His curly hair was exactly like her own - the colour of spun gold. His eyes darkened to the brown of his doting father, and he walked with Declan's gait on his sturdy little legs. It was so easy to want to spoil him.

Luke was a little over two years old when his mother became more and more concerned about him. He was not talking. His developmental checks at the clinic did not show anything untoward. She queried his lack of words, but the nurse assured her that it was early days yet and he would be checked again in six months.

When he was three years old, they took him to the children's play day in the village, but he showed no interest in the children's games or toys there. A snatch of that Phil Coulter song flashed on her mind – 'just like all the others but they know he's not the same' - as Luke turned his back on other children and refused to join in the fun.

Patricia was concerned, but Declan put it down to shyness. She had her doubts. There was something wrong with the child, and she was determined to have him properly assessed. Every time she took him to the clinic, he behaved impeccably. The nurses drooled over him and he smiled a sweet smile for them. Patricia shook her head and began to doubt her own instincts.

That was when she began to notice something else - Luke had some kind of aversion towards her. Despite all her care and attention he did things specifically to annoy her. He knocked over a jug of milk on the table one day. Patricia took it to be an accident, but when he did it again shortly afterwards she knew that he was testing her. She watched out for other things and found them. When her car keys went missing, she found them down the toilet, then her makeup was spilled on the newly-changed bed linen and one day her handbag was full of earth.

It was time for action.

When she voiced her fears to Declan, he laughed and assured her that every child in the world did those kinds of things. It was just being mischievous – his sense of humour. And what was she on about? Luke not talking? He would have plenty to say when he was ready. Her husband dismissed the very thought of taking Luke for further investigation.

'Nothing wrong with the child,' he insisted, 'only too much molly-coddling. He needs to be outdoors more. I should spend more time with him.'

She tried to reason with Declan, but he refused to listen. Patricia realised that she had a major battle on her hands. She had never known her husband to be so adamant. He always bowed to her every wish up until now. Somehow, Patricia, after a lot of persuasion, convinced Declan to let her take Luke to be examined by a recommended child psychologist in Dublin. The diagnosis was autism, and the specialist pulled no punches - the worst scenario was painted for her.

Time Frames and Windows of Recognition and the importance of immediate action were all explained to her, and she was given a fist-full of literature on the vagaries of autism. Patricia cringed. Luke was just a baby, her baby. And lines of the Phil Coulter song kept ringing in her head – 'See the child with the golden hair and eyes that show the emptiness inside.' This was her Luke.

When they got home, she polished a very high shine on the facts for Declan, side-stepping the real issue, afraid the diagnosis would have a profound effect on her husband. And, sure enough, Declan dismissed the consultant's diagnosis, insisting that Luke was perhaps a little slow but would improve gradually, and eventually would talk when he was ready.

'You talk too much yourself, Patricia. You don't let the child get a word in edgeways.'

Day after day, he insisted there was nothing wrong with Luke. Nothing at all. But just to please her, he suggested they seek another opinion. The diagnosis was still the same. There was no way of avoiding it.

She thought of having to face Declan again. She needed some time to calm herself and, going through Parnell Square on the way back to the Bus Arus, she decided to go into the Hugh Lane Gallery for some peace and quiet. When she came upon the Harry Clarke stained-glass window, she halted and, out of the corner of her eye, she saw Luke staring at it. She could see that he, too, was mesmerised by the depiction of Keats' poem St. Agnes Eve.

The following morning Patricia put paper and colouring pencils on the kitchen table hoping that Luke would occupy himself while she did the household chores. That was when he drew the picture that had her gasping in astonishment. The Harry Clarke window.

She couldn't wait for Declan to come home to tell him about it. But instead of being pleased Declan became angry, accusing her of pressuring Luke into doing things that he wasn't capable of. Was she trying to put him on a pedestal and he would be ridiculed by the entire town. Where was this picture now?

She showed him the chewed-up bits. And would Luke draw another one for her? She looked at Luke. No. Of course not. The child looked at her with what seemed to be absolute scorn in his eyes.

Declan looked from one to the other of them there in the kitchen and made an instant decision. 'No more molly-coddling. Let him be a child. Let him play without pressure and, when the time comes, I will teach him all I know. He will watch and he will learn. I will make a man of him.'

Patricia looked at the defiant stare of Luke and then at the set face of Declan and bit her lip. She knew she must do battle with both of them to get the right kind of help for her child, their child. She would take a leaf out of Declan's book. As he had wooed and won her, against all the odds, with solid determination, she would have to find that same determination. A constant dropping that would wear down a stone. Or would it? There was a possibility that she could lose both her son and her husband now. She had to find a way. Yes, yes, she could do it. She had to.

JACK AND LILY

By MAEVE EDWARDS

Bray, Co. Wicklow

The day that Lily volunteered to work in the hospice was the beginning a new life for her following the death of her beloved husband.

'The light bulbs, Lily? Will I change them for you? I brought the ladder.' Jack stood in front of Lily at the reception desk, a questioning expression on his face, a step-ladder by his side. She had been looking out the window at the evening sky and wasn't paying attention. Normally, when Jack came to the hospice to visit his wife, it was pitch dark outside. But tonight, it seemed brighter and the light was different.

'What did you say, Jack? I'm sorry, I was miles away!'

'The light bulbs? There are two of them gone in that fitting over your head. It's like you're sitting in the dark. Every day I've been meaning to do it.'

'But the hospice handyman is supposed to change bulbs,' she said. 'I've asked him, but he's been so busy.'

'It'll only take a minute. Nobody will be any the wiser.'

The phone rang as Jack set up the ladder and quickly clambered up it to remove the light fitting. Lily picked up the receiver and handed Jack the bulbs one by one as his outstretched hand reached down.

'St. Michael's Hospice,' she said. 'Hold one moment and I'll put you through.'

Within seconds, Jack had finished. 'There. All done.' Lily smiled her thanks at him as he refolded the ladder. What a kind man he is, she thought. What a burden he's carrying inside himself and yet he never, ever shows it.

Jack's wife, Miriam, was in Room No. 7. She had been admitted to the hospice just after Christmas and, over the intervening weeks, Lily and she had become friends. They shared an interest in crosswords, and Lily took great delight in watching Miriam open up the crossword page of the newspaper each day, sharpen up her pencil, and set to. But it was clear she was getting weaker. Lily knew the signs only too well as her own husband had died in the very same room only four years earlier.

'I'm off home now,' she told Jack when he returned from putting the ladder back in his van. 'Tell Miriam I'll be in to see her in the morning with her newspaper.'

'Thanks again for buying it for her every day,' he said. 'It means so much to her to get it first thing.'

'It's a pleasure. Good night, Jack. See you tomorrow.'

Lily tidied up her desk and switched the phones through to Val who took over the night shift. 'I'm off now, Val. I'll see you tomorrow.'

The usual despondency settled on her as she walked to her car. The sky in the west had a definite pink tinge to it, and the chestnut tree was showing signs of budding, but even these small signs that spring was on its way failed to lift her spirits. She sat in the car for a moment, her hand on the ignition.

What on earth would she do if she didn't have the hospice to go to? It had been the saving of her after Mike had died. What good sense had made her pick up the phone, on a day just like this one, and offer her services: 'I'd like to volunteer to work in the hospice. My husband died there a few months ago and I want to express my thanks. I have office experience.'

And so it was. Before long, she was doing mornings on reception, then afternoons, and now she was here three and a half days a week. 'You're almost running the place,' her two daughters had said, proud that their mother was creating a new life for herself. But it was more than that. Lily felt she was part of a warm community of people, almost like a family. Most of the voluntary staff had come to work in St. Michael's because their loved ones had died there. She was not wrong when she told her friends that the atmosphere was special. 'It's as if we are surrounded by goodness. Laugh if you like, but it's true.'

Life was still hard, though, without Mike. She had managed to get through the big events, like Christmas and Easter and family gatherings, but it was the small things that got to her. Her two daughters, Claire and Fiona, were good to her, but they had their own lives and homes to think about. She had to stand on her own two feet.

Yes, it was the little things, like coming home in the evenings to an empty house and Mike not being there. It was as simple as that. Only last week she had put the kettle on for a cup of tea and had taken down two cups from the cupboard, forgetting, for one foolish moment, that he was gone. The tears that sprang to her eyes did not surprise her, for she knew they were always there waiting, just under the surface.

'I miss you Mike. I miss you,' she'd cried, as she leaned against the kitchen worktop, still holding the second cup in her hand.

She had kept his favourite tweed jacket as well, had hidden it away from her daughters. They had insisted that she clear out his clothes thinking, probably quite correctly, that she needed to move on.

'Dad's gone three years, Mom, you have to pack his clothes away.' And she had allowed them to come to her bedroom with a large suitcase, and false good humour. She had allowed them to be kind to her as she sat on the bed rigid with grief as memory after memory got pushed down hard into a black plastic sack.

But she had kept his tweed jacket, and every now and again, when she moved something so that it hung there right before her eyes, she would clutch the sleeve of it, hold it to her cheek and let the tears flow.

'Oh, what a foolish woman I am,' she would say to herself. But these moments of sadness were good for her. She was able to pull herself back together again afterwards, stick out her chin and get on with her life.

It was dark now in the car park as she turned the ignition and started the engine. Then a thought came to her. Last autumn she'd planted dozens of daffodil bulbs and this morning when she'd left home, she'd noticed that one of them was bravely attempting to flower in the garden, despite the cold. Tonight, when she got home, she'd take it inside to the windowsill and watch it unfurl its petals. Tomorrow she'd bring it to Miriam and put it in a small vase by her bed. This thought soothed her as she made her way home.

As the days passed, Miriam grew weaker. She was no longer able to summon up the strength to finish the crossword. 'You do it for me, Lily.' And Lily would sit beside the bed and fill in the missing boxes, trying to be cheerful as Miriam's life ebbed away from her, just like Mike's had done four years before.

Soon, Jack and his two sons were at the hospice all the time. They took it in turns to sit beside Miriam's bedside, and every day one or other of them would stop and have a word with Lily at the reception desk.

'At least we're getting a chance to say goodbye to her,' Jack said sadly one day. 'Some families are not that lucky. But you know all about that too, don't you, Lily?'

On a cold clear morning in the middle of March, Lily was met at the door of the hospice by Val.

'Miriam died in the middle of the night,' she said. 'Jack and the boys were by her side.'

At the funeral, Lily sat at the back of the church not wanting to intrude on the small family gathering. The memory of Jack's stricken face remained with her for many days. 'Thank you for coming,' was all he could say.

Afterwards, she missed her morning conversations with Miriam, and Jack's comforting presence each evening. But life was like that at the hospice. You came close to people, and then they were gone.

Spring came in earnest. Her daffodils flowered and they warmed her heart every time she looked at them. In the summer, her daughter, Claire, visited with the news that she and her husband, Tom, were going to have a baby. Lily was going to be a grandmother! She hugged Claire to her, her eyes beaming with delight. How Mike would have thrilled to hear this news.

Her second daughter, Fiona, got engaged that autumn and was planning her wedding. The girls' relationship with her was more equal now and they no longer felt she needed looking after. But sometimes Lily wondered if she'd been too independent, too hasty in pushing them away from her. Christmas came and went and only people who knew Lily well, were aware that she carried loneliness deep inside her.

It was on an ordinary day the following spring that Jack called to the hospice to see her.

'I was passing and thought I'd drop in to see how you are,' he said. He was just as he always had been - calm and steady.

'I often think about you and your boys,' she said all in a rush. 'You get so close to people in here and then suddenly they are gone.'

Why should she feel such joy to see him?

'How've you all been since Miriam died?' she asked. 'How are your two sons?'

'We're all right. We're getting there,' he said. 'Some days are hard, some days not so hard. The boys are great, but I don't want to be a burden to them.'

Lily remembered those early months after Mike's death and all the difficulties she had encountered. She knew what he was going through.

Jack paused and took a moment before he started again.

'I was wondering - and say 'no' now if you don't agree - but I got a present of six tickets to the Leonard Cohen concert. I don't know if you like Leonard Cohen, but I'm going with the boys and their girlfriends, and we were wondering who we could give the sixth ticket to. Then Peter, my oldest boy, said: 'Dad, why don't you ask Lily at the hospice to come with us.' And that's why I'm here.' His voice faltered and then it stopped abruptly.

'I love Leonard Cohen,' was all she could say.

'Are you sure?' He seemed surprised. 'Do you want to ring me later? I'll leave you my number.'

'No, I'd like to go. I'm sure I'd like to go.'

'It's not till June so you have weeks to think about it. And - I didn't tell you this before - but we're all going in my van. It has seats that fold down - you wouldn't mind that, would you? Going in the van, I mean?'

'I've always wanted to go somewhere in a van,' she said simply. 'Doesn't yours have flowers painted on it?'

'Yes, it does,' he said. They stood smiling at each other for what seemed like a very long time. Then he said: 'I'm very pleased you're coming with us. I'll give you a call in a few days.'

Lily said goodbye to him and waved as he went out the door. Why were her cheeks burning? And why was her heart beating so wildly? It was nothing. Nothing at all. Jack and his sons were being kind to her, that was all. He was lonely, just like she was.

Outside, she noticed the cherry tree beside her window had started to bloom. Before long, it would be a riot of pink and white blossoms, their petals falling all around. How had she not noticed it before?

THE GLIMMER MAN

A MEMORY BY **LORNA VINALL**
Poole, Dorset, England

The punishment exacted by the Glimmer Man turned out to be a blessing in disguise.

In 1945, the cold January winds brought snow. One bleak icy afternoon, my sister and I hurried home from school to find my mother standing pale and distressed in our little kitchen. We stood motionless with fear. I was eight years old.

'The Glimmer Man came,' she blurted out, trying not to cry, 'and now we're cut off.'

My heart sank. I knew all about the Glimmer Man - everyone did. He was the man who came knocking on our doors to check that nobody was using 'the glimmer' on the gas stove.

I knew the gas was cut off for several hours every day and that only a glimmer of gas remained on the gas cooker at these times. I knew it was forbidden to use the glimmer and that the government sent 'glimmer men' to call at people's houses when they weren't expecting them, and punish people who were found using the glimmer of gas. I also knew that if you answered the door, they would barge straight into the kitchen and if the stove was hot, you were in trouble.

On this day, we were caught, and, as a punishment, our gas supply was to be completely cut off for two whole weeks. I was frightened to see my mother's anguished face.

Most people took a chance and used the glimmer, and we had evaded the Glimmer Man on numerous occasions.

On our road, we had a system that worked perfectly. When the Glimmer Man called at the first house, a messenger would be surreptitiously sent to warn the next door neighbour, who in turn called over the back garden to the next house and so on from house to house. Many times I was sent to warn others. By the time he had knocked on a few houses, the red alert had

121

spread far and wide. Those who were guilty laid low and didn't answer the door. Unfortunately, my mother, who was partially deaf, had not received the garden warning that day and was caught red-handed.

The three of us clung to each other. Dad was far away in England trying to find work, and we were sad and cold and 'cut off'.

The bad news travelled like lightning. My mother had told Mrs. Colgan next door, and within minutes the gloomy tidings had spread to everyone on the road –'Creenans are cut off.'

But even as we stood in misery in our kitchen, a virtual army of neighbours was networking on our behalf. And even faster and mightier than the bitter winds that were blowing, came an avalanche of help sweeping through our door.

People, who had little or nothing themselves, bombarded us with kindness. They brought electric heaters and electric 'rings'. They baked for us and showered us with kind words. They brought piping hot stews and tasty pies. We may have been punished for two weeks, but now we were rewarded with an abundance of good things - more than we had ever known.

Every morning my mother cooked our porridge in the bedroom on the little 'ring' and we had happy little picnics in bed. Each day brought new surprises and challenges and with every door knock came a cheery band of friends bringing baskets of home baking and warm hearts. Life was so good and such fun.

The arrival of the gas man two weeks later to reconnect us was a sad return to earth. We had savoured the high living for two beautiful weeks and now we had gas again. We were returned once more to normal life.

I'll never forget the Glimmer Man episode. The loving concern of people on the road for each other provided a tower of strength for us all. I had nothing and grew up among people who had very little, but during all that time I never wanted for anything.

Bless them all.

A Passion For Lilies

RICHARD LYSAGHT
Walkinstown, Dublin

*A telephone call revives half-forgotten memories of a youthful
love affair and dreams of what might have been.*

'What would his mother say?' He got up from the table,
scraping his chair against the stone floor and, holding a mug
of tea in his right hand, walked over and stood in the wash
of sunlight pouring through the open door. He gazed across
the fields, oblivious of the chitter-chatter of birds, and, for the
thousandth time since the phone call on Sunday night, agonised
about what he should do.

It was a pointless exercise, for the bouquet of lilies,
wrapped in cellophane and held together by a big red ribbon,
bore testament of his intentions. Still, despite the flowers,
half of himself was uneasy and wanted to kick the other half
for not letting the phone ring through to answer-call. He
only picked it up because he was certain he was going to be
told some of his cattle were out on the back road again - he
really had to stop depending on bits of rope to keep the gate
closed.

He swallowed a mouthful of tea, his mind drifting to
Sunday night.

'Is that Michael Maher?'

Already, his bare feet were on the wooden floor, his right
hand reaching for his trousers flung over the back of the
chair beside his bed.

'Do you know who this is?'

The slight Australian accent threw him. He blinked the
sleep from his eyes, his brain scrambling through memory
banks to match a face to the voice.

'Oh sweetheart, please don't say that you have forgotten
me.'

'Deirdre Lawlor,' he said, recognition making his heart jump.

'Hurray, for a second there, I thought you had forgotten all about me. I mean it has only been ten-years - can you believe it - since we last saw each other.' She laughed her silky laugh, huskier than he remembered, but still managing to draw a finger along his spine.

'How are ye?'

'Okay,' he mumbled, not sure he wasn't dreaming.

'Sorry for the late call, in more ways than one,' she laughed again, 'but I had to wait for my only child, Tracey, to go to bed. I brought her with me to Dublin to see the last surviving member of this branch of the Lawlor clan: my aunt Molly, who is supposed to be ailing, but I can tell you if I'm half as feisty as she is when I am eighty, I'll be entering the Sydney marathon. Oh, I hope you haven't got company, such as a wife or a significant other there with you.' she said, her voice full of concern.

'No, I'm on my own.'

'Oh, aren't you the sensible one,' she said, sighing. 'but then you always were. No falling for the lure of far-away places, big city lights, getting married, starting a family, getting divorced, going through hell; though, I have to say, Tracey who is seven, and thinks she is seventeen, is my light from heaven. She's very like me when I was younger, has the blond hair, the blue eyes but not, thank God, the wild streak, though that's not to say that she can't be a stroppy little miss and downright wilful when the mood takes. Still, I suppose, she'd never be her mother's daughter if she hadn't got that trait.'

Deirdre laughed for a few seconds and then said, 'Oh, would you listen to me rabbitting on like a good one. Come on, let's hear what you've been getting up to these last ten years, and no skimping on the juicy love-gossip bits, Michael.'

He took a deep breath. What could he tell her? He had stayed in Balscan with his mother and, other than doing some lake and river fishing, had devoted every waking hour to developing the farm; once a modest holding comprising of a cottage with twenty acres and ten dairy cows; now a holding comprising of a cottage with one hundred and fifty acres, one hundred and twenty dairy cows, and a thriving mushroom farm.

He also had someone working for him. As for his love life, that resided in the left drawer of a dresser: a letter addressed to a match-making agency, written by his mother, in one of her whimsical moments, outlining what sort of a man he was and detailing what sort of a woman he was looking for.

He went to speak but before he did, Deirdre said,: 'Sad about your mother passing away last year. I was very cut-up about not being able to get over for her funeral, but travelling over from Australia takes a bit of planning and besides, I found out too late. Still, I was raging that I didn't make it. Your mother was a treasure; I got on really well with her.'

Michael smiled. The only time he could remember his mother and Deirdre getting on was when they talked about flowers: they both had a passion for lilies.

'I hope you got the card and note I sent. I intended to write a long letter later, but you know me, if I don't do a thing when the thought hits me, I never do it. Still, I'm sure you knew that I was thinking of you, thinking of you an awful lot actually - the great times we shared, how innocent we were. It really is a pity that,' she paused, took a breath and said, 'oops, sorry, promised myself that I wouldn't go down regret street - so much for promises.'

She gave a nervous laugh. 'Anyway, the reason I'm ringing is to let you know that I will be coming down to Balscan on Tuesday; my aunt's insisting that I revisit my roots. I think, to be honest, she just wants rid of me so she can spoil Tracey even more than she has done already.

'I'll be staying with a friend from my school days for one night before coming back to Dublin on Wednesday morning, and I was wondering if there was any way that you could meet me at the station - train gets in at half- past eleven in the morning. I would dearly, dearly love to see you,

Michael. And who knows,' she said her voice softening, 'if you twist my arm, just a little, I just might phone my friend and tell her that I will make my own way to her house later, much later. You could drive me to the farm, show me all the improvements you have made, and then maybe we could take a walk down past Morrissey's old house, where we used to do our courting. What do you say?' she said, her voice becoming even softer.

He was unable to say anything: his mouth was dry, his breath was caught in his chest, his heart was thumping, and his whole body was tingling.

'I do hope our courting spot hasn't been razed to the ground, has it?'

'No,' he coughed, forced a breath into his lungs and said, 'it's still there, part of it, at least.'

'Brilliant. I'd love to see it. What do you say? Take a trip back in time.'

'Yes,' he said, nodding his head, 'I'd really like that.'

'Well, you know what to do, Michael Maher; be at Balscan train station before half- past eleven on Tuesday morning, and look out for a woman with plum coloured hair, cropped to her skull. The long blond hair is no more, I'm afraid, but I'm still the same when it comes to being kept waiting, you remember?'

He remembered.

Something soft going round his ankles in a figure of eight brought Michael back to the present. He gazed down at Figaro, his tortoise-shell cat. 'Only being nice to me because you want something.' He said, his thoughts returning to Deirdre, to the last night they stood in what was once the door-way to Morrisey's place. Deirdre had her head nestled under his chin, her arms wrapped around his waist. He had stood lost in the pressing closeness of her body, intoxicated by both the feel and scent of peaches emanating from her blond hair.

'Michael, this is our chance to see the world. With the money left to you from your uncle's will, and with what I have saved, we can easily afford to head off for a year. Oh, I know that you're mad for developing the farm, but we can both settle down and do that when we come back. You can get someone to look after the farm while we're away, and to keep an eye on your mother. And before you say it, I know she is fairly bad with arthritis, but she's well able to get around, and we will be back in a year, maybe sooner.'

She tightened her arms around his waist. 'I am so excited. I just can't wait to see Rome, Paris, New York, Sydney...' she went on till she ran out of cities, and then she tilted her head and looked up at him with twinkling china-blue eyes and said: 'You could tell your mother tonight. What do you say?'

He said nothing, just kissed her.

Michael turned from the door and walked over to the dresser; Figaro following with his tail erect. Michael opened a tin of kitty-kat, emptied the contents on to a saucer. He placed the saucer down in front of Figaro, straightened and focussed his attention on the photograph of his mother in the centre of the dresser. He shook his head. The strange thing was had his mother agreed with his plan to leave, he definitely would have left with Deirdre, but his mother just sat in a chair, hands knitted together, each finger tip touching a knuckle the size of an angry bunion, and, in a calm voice, said: 'If you think that you can make this woman happy and know in your own heart that you won't be miserable for putting aside the opportunity to realise your dream of developing the farm, then you go with my every blessing.'

'I wonder what you would say now, Mother, about me meeting Deirdre?' He shifted his gaze to the photograph beside his mother's: the photograph of a smiling twenty-year-old Deirdre. For several minutes he stood marvelling at her flawless beauty until the thought of her blond hair cropped and plum coloured pushed a stone into his heart. 'How could you do such a thing? Such beautiful hair.'

He sighed long and hard, and then he shook his head and said in a forlorn voice, 'time to go.' He glanced at his mother's photograph, and suddenly, he could hear her saying: 'Is it the Deirdre that shared neither your dream for the farm nor your love of the land that you are so anxious to meet, or is it the girl in the photograph whose beauty you fell in love with?'

He looked again at the photograph of Deirdre; the realization that he had been in love with a vision, a vision of pure loveliness and nothing else, dawning on him. 'Am I really that shallow?' The stone in his heart was pushed aside by a bigger stone. He sighed, long and hard, and then he opened the drawer, took out the letter addressed to the 'new-friends matching agency', placed the photograph of Deirdre in the drawer, and walked over and picked up the bouquet of lilies.

Outside, he paused to stroke Figaro, who had returned to indulging in his favourite pastime when the sun was shining: lying fully stretched out on the garden wall.

'You might be getting fresh fish for tea, Figaro, depending on how they're biting.'

Figaro opened his eyes and arched his body to get the full benefit of the stroke along his back. 'First, though, I think I'll take these flowers to the mother's grave and then post a letter. What say you to that?'

Figaro yawned, settled his body back down on the wall, closed his eyes and dozed.

UNCLE JACK

BY PATRICIA O'FLAHERTY
Castletroy, Limerick

It became more and more difficult for Uncle Jack to find work. He joined the crowd at the factory gates and others were taken on, but, more often than not, he would be turned away.

On the day he disappeared, Uncle Jack followed his usual weekday routine of staying under the bedcovers until Nellie shouted at him to get up. He would walk into the city to look for work or go to St Anne's Cathedral where they gave out clothing and food for the families of men who were out of work.

'Are ye gettin' up, Jack? The tea's made and the griddle's hot for yer soda, afore ye go.'

Nellie's voice came floating up the stairs interrupting his reading. The bedroom was strewn with books, piled on top of each other. The piles leaned precariously, some of them pushed over to the wall by Nellie on the rare occasion she came in with a brush and pan to clear some of the dust.

Magazines and newspapers added to the chaos and in the midst of it all lay Jack under the blankets and the bedcover, his head raised by a pillow, the better to read his newspaper, with his cap fitted at a jaunty angle over his mop of red hair and intense blue eyes.

Jack was a big man, physically and in his personality. It was impossible to ignore him. He had worked at the docks, lifting loads too heavy for his fellow workers, his bulk serving him and his family well. Like many men his size, Jack was not physically aggressive. He would walk away when someone tried to pick a fight after too many drinks, but he did love a good verbal argument, preferably about politics.

He had nothing but contempt for the government and thought the divisions in Ireland were cultivated by the mill and shipyard owners. As he expressed this opinion at every opportunity and loudly in his booming voice, his reputation went before him, amongst his working-class companions, but also amongst the ruling classes, those who owned the factories along the shoreline in Belfast and the men who ran the shipyard and its huge work force.

It became more and more difficult for him to find work. He joined the crowd at the factory gates and others were taken on, but he would, more often than not, be turned away. The foremen wouldn't look him in the eye; they lowered their gaze or looked over his head, as they shook their heads.

The turn of the century hadn't made any difference to the lot of the working man, despite promises from the new Labour Party. Robert Cecil, Lord Salisbury and his conservatives had won the Khaki election, so-called because the British soldiers, in their new khaki uniforms, were fighting those elusive horsemen, the Boers and that war was the main issue of the election. But the Irish Nationalists had 82 seats and, had, therefore, to be contended with, whether the Tories liked it or not.

While reading last night's Tele, Jack savoured the sensation of the warmth and comfort afforded by the big bed, the mattress of which was hollowed to accommodate two sleeping bodies curled together. Reluctantly, he swung his legs out of the covers and placed his two bare soles on the wooden floor, cradling his head in his hands, until he got his balance and raised his head.

He pulled on his trousers, fished a heavy, rough woven cotton shirt out from under a pile of un-ironed washing, wriggled his head and arms into a dark blue pullover and retrieved his tweed jacket from the banister, where he'd hung it last night on his way in from the pub.

Aunt Nellie was barely five feet tall, with a thick plait of dark hair wound around her head. She wore an apron over a plain brown dress and her sleeves were pushed up over strong forearms, used to kneading dough and handling babies. Her feet were clad in a pair of Jack's thick socks and pushed into worn slippers. She was a pretty woman and her carefree, cheerful nature overcame the signs of ageing which would have stolen the looks of a more serious-minded woman, faced with the daily chores demanding Nellie's attention.

'Oooh! Lovely cuppa, love, nice and hot,' mumbled Jack through a half-eaten soda.

'No butter, can't be helped. That old skinflint Flanagan wouldn't give me credit. Said there'd be no more credit 'till we paid the bill. If you get any work today, we'll have to pay off a bit of it to keep him quiet.'

'I'll be off then. I'll get some flour and butter in Flanagan's on the way back and I'll pay some of the bill. What do we owe him?'

'Four pounds, three shillings and six pence. If you give him two pounds, he'll put the flour and butter on the tick. Come straight back, now, and don't go anywhere near McNamara's.'

Wee Nellie, her mother's namesake, and Hughie came in an hour later from school. She gave them tea and the rest of the soda. Then, Lily and wee Tommy, after his uncle, threw their school bags on the hall floor. They were in the big school and came home later. The baby woke and needed feeding. Would Jack never get back? If he'd gone into that pub, she'd kill him.

'Lily, mind the wee'uns 'till I go down to your Aunt Susie's. I won't be long.'

She took her coat from the hook in the hall, changed slippers for ankle boots and went out into the cold air. The house was set at the top of a flight of steps and, before starting down the steps, Nellie looked out over the roof tops and onto the shore of Belfast Lough with the harbour and the shipyard beyond. The house was one of a row of red brick houses in Seaview, a district inhabited mainly by shipyard workers. There was another row of houses beneath their street and a row above and behind them, as the houses were built on the side of a hill.

She hurried down the street and into the next one, where her sister, Susie, lived. Susie and Thomas ran a small grocer's shop on the Shore Road. They had lived above the shop until a few months ago, when a house became vacant near Nellie and Jack.

Susie and Nellie had taken turns queuing at the Council offices to plead their case. They had to queue for days, marking their spot with a bag of rags at night when the offices closed and taking up the space in the queue at opening time in the morning. The houses were part of a new scheme of letting with an option to buy and hundreds of people had applied from North Belfast.

'Could you lend me some butter and a few spuds,' Nellie blurted out, as soon as she got in the door. 'Jack's still not home and they've all to be fed. I'll bring them back in the morning.'

Susie didn't have a chance to say 'yes' or 'no' as Nellie was gone almost as soon as she burst in. Armed with the potatoes and the butter, she charged back home and set to making the tea, forgetting for the meantime about Jack and the missing flour and butter.

She began to worry when the next day came and went and there was still no sign of Jack. He'd never gone off before without saying anything. She went to the police station.

'Maybe he just went off for a bit of a jaunt,' the sergeant leaned on the counter pretending to take notes.

She could tell he wasn't interested and was thinking 'Was it any wonder he went off, with so many mouths to feed?'

So, that was no good. She borrowed money from Susie to keep them going and tried not to think about it too much, just got on with things. Luckily, there was always Mrs Boyle's washing coming in. That made a bit of money, enough to buy more potatoes, milk and pay for a bag of coal.

A week went by. She called in at all the usual haunts, McNamara's, the bookie's, even the shipyard, in case he'd got work. Susie said to go to Seaview Church, tell the Reverend Brown that Jack had done a runner, even though she didn't really think he had and that was what was worrying her, and to get some money from the charity case box.

The old grandfather clock in the hall ticked very loudly at night when the children were finally asleep and the bed seemed very big without Jack spreading his bulk over it.

Ten days after he had gone, the children had just left for school and she was having a drop of tea before starting the washing. She jumped as the letter box banged. The house was so quiet without Jack, even though he spent the mornings in bed reading, she could feel his presence and he would shout out every now and again, reading her bits out of the paper and criticising the politicians.

Nellie ran to the door and was in time to see the postman tripping down the steps and into her neighbour's garden. There was a large, brown envelope lying on the mat, with a line of colourful stamps across the corner. She took a step back from it, as if it was dangerous. 'Don't be silly. Open it and maybe there'll be some news.'

'Nellie, my love,' she heard Jack's voice in her head as she read the letter, 'the recruiters were at the dock when I got there. I had done the rounds of the factories and the shipyard. Here's the cheque for £23 from my first pay. Take it to the post office and cash it. I'll send more as soon as I can. I joined up. We're training in England. We'll be going to South Africa. I never thought I'd be fighting on the side of the English, but the wee 'uns have to be fed and schooled somehow. There's good men here. Everyone sticks together and the officers aren't too bad, except for one stuck-up toff.

'Don't you worry yourself. You know, I'm strong and have a good head on my shoulders. Just you mind yourself and the childer. I'll be home after the training and will have more news then. You can write to the address at the top of the letter and I'll get it in a couple of days. I hope you are all well. I know this must be a bit of a shock, but everything will be better now that I'm earning some money. I knew Susie and the Reverend Brown would help you out 'till I could send you word.

Your loving husband, Jack.'

Nellie sat down with a bump on the hall chair. What was he thinking of. Going to England! Joining the British army! She knew work was hard to find now in Belfast and Jack had no trade, but surely it hadn't come to this. South Africa meant the Boer War. She didn't have time to read the paper like Jack, but he talked enough about the government and the goings-on, what with Home Rule and Tories and Whigs and dear knows what else, she knew enough to be worried. Going out to foreign parts, getting speared or, worse, eatin' by savages, dear goodness, what was she going to do?

Well, one thing was sure and certain, there was nothing she could do. She'd better do as he said, cash the cheque and pay Flanagan. She'd get spuds, butter, milk and maybe a bit of brisket and coal and pay Susie back. Oh no, she'd have to tell Susie and Thomas. They always said Jack was feckless. Now they'd never give over.

Uncle Jack didn't come home on leave before he sailed from Southampton late one spring evening to make the three-week journey across the Bay of Biscay, calling at Madeira and along the west coast of Africa to dock at Cape Town's beautiful harbour. He came home three long years later, unrecognisably changed into a thin, tanned man, whose heavy muscular bulk had disappeared, who looked much older than his forty-five years and who never spoke of his life as a soldier in the Boer War.

FATHER LOVE

A MEMORY BY PAULINE O'HARE
Balbriggan, Co. Dublin

A child's troubled thoughts become the key to the discovery of a father's love.

When I was nine, the thought of dying tormented me, and I would lie awake at night, crying into my pillow, as I tried to come to terms with both mortality and infinity. Often my sobs drew my mother to my bedside where she would sit and stroke my forehead to calm me to sleep.

The death of Mrs Johnston - the mother of my best friend Anna - changed all that. On the morning of her funeral, as the coffin was carried out of the church, Mr Johnston tried to stretch his arms over the shoulders of his four children, two on either side of him, as tears coursed unheeded down his cheeks. At that moment, I understood, for the first time, how the cold and unfeeling finger of death could destroy happiness as quickly as the altar servers had snuffed out the candles at the end of the funeral Mass.

I began to cry. What would become of them all, without a mother? Never again would they feel the warmth of her unspoken love. All those tiny things, which were so important - like the clink of her wedding ring on the rolling pin as she made an apple tart – would be gone. And when I thought of a mother's healing kiss, I wept louder.

As I stood at the graveside, that sunny June morning, I believed, in my childlike innocence, that it would be better for a father to die than a mother. I began to wonder what would become of me if my own mother died. How could I survive without her? I shivered at the thought, opening my eyes just as the coffin was lowered into the grave.

I was immediately confused by what I saw. Anna's sister was crying. Mr Johnston bent down, lifted her up and cuddled her close. At the same time, he took a handkerchief from his pocket and wiped away Anna's tears.

The two other children hung around his legs, their heads against his stomach. He could have been their mother, so automatic his responses, so natural his comforting. How could this be so? He was, like my father, a farmer whose days were spent outdoors, his life dictated by the whims of the weather and the needs of the animals. Household matters were mysteries to both men.

I looked across at my father on the opposite side of the grave and wondered if he would be like Mr Johnston, if my mother died. Even at the age of nine, I knew it was wrong to think like that, but I couldn't help it.

My troubled thoughts came home with me; that night I could not sleep. I had to find out if my father could love me like a mother. So I began to shadow him around the farm. If he found strange, my sudden appearance by his side, he never questioned it, nor did he make me feel the nuisance I, undoubtedly, must have been.

It rained a lot that summer. We spent many hours in the barn repairing machinery. I learned to hammer and paint, and how to use a drill, and my father talked to me about his childhood and of his own father, his tales as entertaining as any bedtime stories. And if he did not kiss my fingers when I hit them with a hammer, the cold water from the outside tap that he ran over them had the same soothing effect, while the lingering smell of tobacco on his clothes was as comforting as the smell as my mother's freshly-made bread.

I remember one day, as we were repairing hay-rakes, Rover, the sheepdog, limped in, put his head on my father's lap, looked up at him and whined and my father said: 'Show me, old boy.' Rover lifted his paw, and I watched as my father removed a thorn with such tenderness that a lump came to my throat.

Gradually, I realised that love was many different things, none of which could be measured or compared. If it was there in the tender hands of my mother as she sewed and cooked and soothed my hurts, it was also there in the gentle touch of my father's rough hand on my head, as he passed behind my chair, or when he plaited baler twine into a rope to make me a swing.

Before long, I discovered what I already knew: he could never love me like my mother, or ever replace her, no more than she could love me like him or replace him, for, if she was my guiding star, he was my anchor.

And somewhere along the way, I forgot about dying and got on with living, and loving.

THE AMERICAN WAKE

By MARY DWYER
Glasnevin North, Dublin

Molly's mother knew deep down that those who went to America were never coming back. It broke her heart to know she would never see her daughter again.

M olly stood at the cottage door with an ache in her heart, watching and waiting. The previous night she had quarrelled and bade farewell to her darling boy. Then all night long she had tossed and turned. Whenever she closed her eyes, his face was in front of her. Blue eyes fringed with black lashes, dark curly hair and a smile that would melt ice. That was her Jimmy. Now no longer her Jimmy, she thought.

In the distance she heard the sound of horse's hooves and her heart leapt inside her. But she was disappointed to see that it was a pony and trap bringing yet more visitors to the already crowded cottage.

It was Molly Power's American wake. Tomorrow she would set foot from Faithlegge in County Waterford on her long journey to America. The year was 1865 and Molly was eighteen years old.

The new arrivals greeted her in the old familiar Waterford way.

'Well girl,' and she answered 'Well girl' or 'Well boy' as the case might be. The older folk shook her hand and enquired about her health. Her mother rushed across and fussed over them. They were the O'Briens who had a farm a few miles away. They had not been evicted like the Powers and many hundreds of others like them during the Great Famine in the eighteen forties. In spite of this, the families had remained friends.

Molly's family no longer had a pony and trap. After the eviction, her father had been lucky to get work as a farm labourer on a big estate. Since then, instead of a farmhouse, they lived in a labourer's cottage.

Mrs Power always said that God had been very good to them. They could have finished up wandering the roads like so many of their friends. Even so, times were very hard and feeding her large family had always been her main worry.

By now two sons had gone to America, one daughter was in service in Co. Kildare and the last one to leave had gone to England. As they could not write, the Powers seldom heard from them except the odd note which would have been written for them and read in Faithlegge by someone who could read. Now there would be just three younger ones left behind after Molly went.

Mrs. Power lived for her children and dreaded the painful partings. Deep down, she knew that those who went to America were never coming back. Already, she had lost two children during the Famine. She blamed herself when her milk dried up and she could not feed them. This left them delicate from birth and, in her heart, she knew they would be taken from her at an early age. But the pain of emigration was just as bad, even though she kept telling herself that her children were still alive. Every night she prayed that someday they would meet again.

Her eldest son, Mikey, was the first to emigrate. Then a few years later they got word that he had a job in a pool hall. They puzzled about this. What was a pool hall? How could there be a pool in a hall? Nobody seemed to know the answer.

A month or so before this night, a letter had come from Mikey in America. It wasn't a real letter, more a note.

'Dear Mother,

'Just a few lines to let you know that I am well. I hope you are too. The enclosed dollars are to pay Molly's passage to America.

Your son,

Mikey'

Molly Power did not want to go to America but had no choice. Now here she was keeping her lonely vigil by the door. For the last time she took in all that was happening. She looked at the faces of her loving family and friends. She listened to their voices. She heard the giggles of her two young sisters as they fixed each other's hair. She could smell the bread baking on the griddle. She could smell the turf fire and knew this was the smell she would miss most of all.

Her mother understood why her daughter stood at the door and she kept trying to distract her by calling her in to make more tea, or put the kettle on the hob or hand around the currant bread.

Her father was busy scratching away at his old fiddle as if his life depended on it. But now and then he would play some slow airs and the tears would pour down his face. One of his daughters would wipe his eyes with a rag and ask him to play a jig.

Then as many as could would get up on the floor and start to dance. The sparks would fly as the lads danced in their hob-nailed boots and the girls would hold themselves erect as they shyly danced their fancy steps. After that, someone would start singing. All the songs were about people going away and never coming back or about people dying. Every song was accompanied by tears.

Molly's mother called her into the room to sing her Irish song. She obliged and, as she began singing 'Jimmy a mhíle stór,' she instinctively knew that her Jimmy had come into the kitchen. She fought back the tears as she sang in Irish about 'Jimmy who went to sea and never returned.' But Molly was the one who was going away and never returning.

Everyone clapped when she finished and Molly ran out the door quickly followed by Jimmy. Her father played some dance tunes and the young people got up to dance again.

Outside, Jimmy put his arms around her and she cried quietly on his shoulder.

'Asthore, I was afraid I wouldn't see you before I left. I spoke so many harsh words last night. I'd have carried them all the way to America and they would have festered inside me for the rest of my life.'

'O Molly, you were right, but I couldn't accept it. Now I know you were talking sense but it doesn't make it any easier.

It's hopeless. Last night I never closed an eye and first thing this morning I told my father I wanted to have a serious talk with him. And we talked for a long time. I told him the way I felt about you and that I wanted to marry you.'

He said: 'Listen to me, son. I'm sorry for you. Molly is a nice girleen, but you cannot marry her. She has no fortune, and I have to find fortunes for your two sisters or we'll have them on our hands forever.'

'I got very angry and threatened to follow you to America, but that made him furious.'

'Do if you want to but, by the Lord Harry, you'll leave Waterford without a penny of money from me and you needn't show your face here again. Farmers can't afford romance. It was the same in my time. Your grandfather picked your mother for me. She had a fortune. I'll never forget the first time I saw the sulky face on her. It was at the chapel the morning of the wedding. She was years older than me. But I got used to her and we're still together in spite of everything.'

Jimmy said: 'Molly, I have an idea who he has picked for me and I hate the thought of her and her whole family.'

Deep down, Molly knew as well. It was Lizzie O'Brien who was always visiting Jimmy's home with her mother. Now she was smugly sitting inside the cottage just biding her time.

She knew that as sure as night followed day, Lizzie would take her place but she hoped never in Jimmy's heart.

For the last time they walked arm-in-arm to where Jimmy's horse was tethered.

'Whatever happens, Molly darling, I promise you one thing. I will never love anyone the way I love you.'

One last kiss and he got on the horse and rode away without looking back. As Molly went back to the cottage, she felt that half of her heart had gone down that road with him.

She heard some of the visitors asking her mother, Kitty to sing. Poor Kitty was too tired and sad so Molly went in to sing along with her.

It was a song that was always sung at these times.

'Asthore Machree, when you're far away from the home you'll soon be leaving,

'Tis many a time through the night and the day, that your heart will be sorely grieving,

The strangers' land may be bright and gay, and rich in its treasures golden,

But you'll pine I know for the long ago and the land that was never olden.'

Molly stopped singing and listened to the sweet voice of her mother, this voice that all her life she had heard soothing sick children or lulling them to sleep at night.

'Next time I hear my mother's lovely voice will be in Heaven.'

Molly's father called her to his side. Mr. O'Leary, a Cork neighbour of theirs, was with him.

'I've been asking himself the best way for you to travel. He's used to the roads. He thinks it would be shorter and safer for you to go the coast road to Cork

Mick O'Leary spoke .

'Now Molly girl, the roads are full of vagrants, all desperate people. Be careful who you speak to. Don't tell your business as they'll know you have your passage money and they'd kill you for it. If you have to, say you're visiting a sick aunt in Cork, but in God's name don't mention Queenstown. But you'll meet lovely people, too, who will give you a cup of tea or even a place to lay your head. Head off for Passage, then Woodstown, then, let me see, Dunmore, then Tramore, Annestown - wait now - Bonmahon then Dungarvan. That's a fine big town. I'll write the names down for you.

You'll know when you don't hear the flat Waterford accents anymore that you're heading for the border and you'll be in Cork before you know it. They'll all be speaking in my lovely sing-song voice.'

With that, he gave Molly a big wink and she laughed for the first time in days.

The party broke up and Molly went to bed but not to sleep.

Next morning bright and early, she was up. She packed her clothes in her bag with her habit (shroud) and a few odds and ends. Two days earlier she had sewn the precious dollars into the hem of her petticoat in case anyone tried to rob her.

After breakfast, she said goodbye to her father who told her to be good and say her prayers and go to Mass on Sundays. Her younger sisters were pulling at her clothes, crying and begging her not to leave them. Her young brother was outside throwing stones and ignoring them all. Molly tore herself away from them and ran to the door followed by her mother who walked down the lane beside her.

She sprinkled Holy Water on her, put her arms around her and whispered:

'What am I going to do without my girrseach. Sure, you're like my right hand. Go in God's name and don't look back.'

They embraced and, for the last time, Molly looked on her mother's careworn face.

On a sunny summer's morning, Molly Power set off for America walking barefoot carrying her bag and her only pair of boots which she was sparing for America.

She was leaving behind everyone and everything she held dear. As she walked she wept quietly, then she sat on a ditch and sobbed her heart out.

'O God help me, what's to become of me at all, at all?'

In time the crying ended.

Then Molly Power pulled herself together and set off down that lonely road to her new life.

CULM

A *MEMORY BY* LIAM POWER

Glendara, Kill, Co. Kildare

Remembering a youthful chore with few redeeming features.

C an you recall the most detestable chore of your childhood? Mine was, without question, having to mix culm, a domestic fuel for burning in an open grate. Many may not have heard of the word, yet around the Castlecomer Collieries of North Kilkenny and the bordering parts of Laois and Carlow it was common up to the early sixties. It was a by-product of anthracite coal-mining, a mix of shingle and dust. In today's terms it might be regarded as cheap, yellow-pack fuel.

This chore, since it happened mainly in winter, had one redeeming feature: it was primarily an indoor task. The qualification refers to the need to get a vital ingredient in a nearby field, a bucketful of yellow clay. In rain and particularly in frost or snow, that task bordered on slavery.

About twice a year, my father went with his old reliable grey mare and cart to the local collieries of either Rossmore or Crettyard. Wooden creels were added to get the maximum load. The ten to twelve mile return journey along rickety roads was a day's work in itself, not to speak of being covered from head to toe with black dust. It was heeled up outside the barn door and shovelled inside with an old wheelbarrow. Since my older brother and sister were at secondary school, the unenviable task of mixing the culm was left with yours truly.

The job was very similar to making a cake without the seasoning. The recipe:

Bed of dry culm – perhaps twenty to thirty shovelfuls in a heap. Bucket of finely chopped yellow clay.

Water as required.Wellingtons were an essential requirement, no need for an apron. The culm and clay were mixed thoroughly with a shovel. A well was made in the heap and water added.

It was blended in from the sides until moist. This was a trial and error exercise. It was now ready for the most laborious part, walking all over the flattened out heap which we called a bed. This latter word I can assure you had nothing to do with 'Odearest' for there was no rest or comfort.

Some people often called this 'Dancing the culm' as in Michael J. Conry's book of the same name. Dancing implied enjoyment, which didn't exist. I preferred to call it trampling, since you had to stomp your feet in a two-step manner, moving back and forth, or in a circular fashion for the best part of an hour. It was a bit like marching on the spot except with a forward motion. Every five minutes you remixed it into a heap with the shovel and repeated this about ten times.

As a nine to twelve year old, and being a six to seven stone weakling, it took much longer to fully bind the mix. Eventually, when I had difficulty lifting my feet from the tacky, glutinous mix I knew it was 'cooked'. That was a really satisfying moment. The bed of culm was heaped up in a corner. To prevent it drying out it was covered with a moist canvas sack.

On reflection, it wasn't all bad, like when, if it happened on a Saturday, my brother or sister might be there to add some stomping feet and lighten the burden. Or, when my sister Nancy was home from England, it was a novelty for her and we'd have great fun. Perhaps only then in my experience 'dancing the culm' might aptly apply.

This was one chore with no shortcuts, as the proof of the pudding was in the burning. A bucketful was brought into our kitchen and put on an already lighted fire in small hand shovelfuls. Alternatively, it was shaped by hand into small oblong shaped culm bombs.

If it was dull and lifeless, frowns and further mixing in the bucket might be needed. If it took off in a while and burned brightly, my parents paid me glowing compliments. The real reward was a cosy warm kitchen on a winter's evening. To boot, the most delicious toast was made when a slice of bread was pierced with a fork and held close to the furnace-like glow until golden brown. Smeared with homemade salty butter it was a feast in itself.

All was well for about another week until the culm heap had dwindled and it was my turn to repeat the whole drab exercise. At the age of thirteen, a life-changing event happened. We had renovations done to the house, the old grate was no more and was replaced by a spanking new cream Wellstood cooker which burned 'real' anthracite. This was a gift from heaven as it ended the most detestable chore of my youth.

A LONG ROAD TRAVELLED

BY DENNIS O'SULLIVAN
Newtownabbey, Co. Antrim

*As he approaches the village, Dan Herlihy feels in his bones
that today is the right day for what he has in mind. The bright
sunlight suddenly breaks through the clouds like an omen that
he has chosen his time well.*

Not a breath of wind disturbs the early morning mist. It hangs like a fine veil softening the outlines of the hills on the far side of the bay. A low blanket of clouds obscures the top half of Muckish mountain. Through the window of his little cottage, Dan Herlihy sees the valley stretching towards the sea in a series of layers, like parts of a stage set, each layer progressively less well defined as the mist imparts its near mystical feel to the view he never tires of looking at.

In time, he knows the mist will be swallowed into the air and absorbed by the earth and sea, leaving a clear bright day with just a hint of autumn coolness. The vermilion heads of Indian corn in the hedgerow bow under the weight of dew. Across the valley a flock of sheep grazes steadily in the field beside the yellow house. A bullock stands on the hill, outlined against the pale grey morning sky.

Dan would be hard pressed to say how often he has sat taking in this familiar landscape. As a small boy it fascinated him. And now, in his sixty-fifth year, it still appeals to him like no other place ever has. Below his cottage, the road to the village twists and turns between the edge of the marshy valley and the steeply rising slopes of the brackened hill. Dan knows every dip, every turn in the road.

As he sips his strong black tea he thinks of the long walk he will make, very soon, along that road. Today, he has important business to do, business that has been left undone too long.

He gives the mist a little longer to lift, then shrugs into his ancient Crombie overcoat, places his battered tweed hat, its band studded with fishing flies, on his head, takes his blackthorn stick in hand and makes his way down the rough lane to the road.

Beneath a mix of grey and fluffy white clouds the water of the bay lies like dull metal. The yellow house no longer offends the eye, having assumed a mellower shade that blends more readily with the surrounding landscape. Muckish still broods half-hidden behind its night cap of wispy cloud. To the east the sky is streaked blue, promising a tussle between the good and the bad. A film of light mizzle softens the far-off outline of Horn Head.

Dan walks steadily, the stick tapping urgently on the metalled road. By the time he reaches the pub overlooking the harbour, he is ready for a rest.

'How's Dan?' The barman is already pulling the pint of Guinness.

Dan looks around. There is only one other customer in the bar - Jimmy O'Driscoll. The two men studiously ignore one another. They haven't exchanged a word for close on ten years.

'Ah, sure, as well as can be expected, Michael. The ould pains are bothering me a bit, but I'm still above ground. That's a grand day, so it is.' Dan takes his usual seat at the corner of the bar from where he can see the activity at the pier.

'It looks like we might get a bit of sun later on.'

Michael places the foaming pint in front of him. Dan breathes a deep sigh, places his hat on the bar and wraps a proprietorial hand around the cool glass. He takes a deep pull, smacks his lips appreciatively.

'Where are you off to this morning then, Dan?'

Dan ignores the question. He takes another sip of his pint, and searches systematically in his coat pockets, eventually finding and withdrawing a briar pipe.

'Now, Dan, you know I can't let you light that up in here. I'm sorry, but it's the law, you know.' Michael speaks nervously, unsure if Dan will pay any attention.

'Is it the law you're citing to me now? Sure there's nobody knows the law better than me. Didn't I have occasion to use it often enough.'

He glances towards Jimmy O'Driscoll.

'You needn't worry, young Michael, I'll not be bothering you by lighting up. I just need a suck on it to go along with my pint.'

'No offence, Dan. Sure I enjoy a smoke myself, but the boss would have my guts for garters if I let anybody light up in here.'

The barman picks up a cloth and rubs vigorously at a glass, holding it to the light to check its cleanness.

'Have you business in the village then, Dan?' Michael tries again.

Dan looks sharply at him. He pauses before answering.

'Ach, I'm just taking a wee walk. At my age you need to keep active. You don't want the old bones to seize up now?'

The barman shrugs his shoulders. He knows that Dan won't tell him anything he doesn't want to tell. No doubt he'll hear in due course, but it might not be from Dan who has a reputation for keeping his business to himself.

The pint finished, Dan bids Michael farewell and strides resolutely from the bar. The sight of Jimmy O'Driscoll has made him even more determined to get his business done as soon as possible.

Approaching the village, Dan's spirits rise. He feels in his bones that today is the right day for what he has in mind. The bright shafts of sunlight that suddenly break through the clouds seem like an omen that he has chosen his time well.

Nellie Hourigan's little house is right in the centre of the main and only street. As Dan lifts the catch on the gate, the sunlight is already picking out the vivid colours of the rambling roses massed around the front porch. He raises the knocker to announce his presence just as the door opens and Nellie appears. With a start she exclaims:

'Why, Dan, you gave me a shock standing there with your arm raised. For a minute I thought you were going to knock me on the head and steal my pension.'

Dan's heart sinks as he sees that Nellie is dressed in her overcoat with a bright red woollen scarf wrapped around her neck. She is a small woman, a sprightly sixty-year-old with a cheerful smile and a head of tightly packed blue grey curls.

'Ach, I see you're on your way out.'

The disappointment in Dan's voice is plain.

'Well, it can wait a wee while, Dan. I was just going up the road to see...'

She leaves the sentence unfinished.

'Come on in and have a cup of tea. I've some nice currant scones just out of the oven.'

Nellie turns on her heel leaving the door open for Dan to follow.

He eases himself into one of the two solid armchairs on either side of the fire, as Nellie busies herself wetting the tea and buttering the scones.

'You've been a bit of a stranger here for the last while, Dan. I thought you'd fallen out with me. Although, God save us all, I couldn't see any reason why you would.'

'Away out o' that with you, Nellie. It'll be a long time before I ever fall out with you. It's just I've had things to think about and I needed a while by myself to work them out.'

Dan shuffles his feet self-consciously, not wanting to say too much too soon.

'And what would you have to be thinking about so hard, Dan. It's devil the thing in the world you have to worry about now.'

Nellie arranges the generously buttered scones on a blue and white ringed plate and pours tea into a pair of matching mugs.

Dan looks up at Nellie as she smilingly hands him his mug of tea and sets the plate on the table between the two chairs.

'Well, now, Dan. This is nice. I enjoy a cup of tea with an old friend.'

Dan eases himself from one hip to the other and sets his mug back on the table. He opens his mouth to speak and then closes it again, like a fish gasping for air. And then he blurts it out.

'Will you step out with me, Nellie?' he says.

Nellie's hand stops halfway to her mouth. The melting butter on the scone slides slowly towards the edge, drips onto the red-tiled floor.

'Well, upon my soul, Dan Herlihy,' she says crossly, rising to get a cloth to wipe up the offending blob of butter. 'Look what you've made me do. If you're going to be making jokes like that you'd be as well to take yourself off home. The tea must be going to your head.'

A slow reddening spreads across Dan's face.

'I'm deadly serious, Nellie. That's what I've been thinking about all these weeks. I want you to marry me.'

Nellie pushes out of her chair, walks to the window overlooking the street and stands there staring out. It seems like an age before she turns back to face Dan.

'It took you long enough to ask and me sitting here, a widow woman, for ten years past without a one to lean on.'

'Ah, Nellie, sure you know it's not right to be rushing such important matters. I wanted to give you proper mourning time for poor Joe. There's hardly a day gone by in all those years I haven't thought about asking you, but somehow it never seemed right, until now, that is. When I sat this morning and looked out across the bay at Muckish and felt the peace and quiet of the valley, I just knew I had to share it - with you, Nellie.'

'Did it never occur to you that you might have left it too late?'

Nellie's words break over Dan like a drench of cold water.

'Jimmy O'Driscoll asked the same question yesterday - for the twentieth time.'

Dan jumps to his feet nearly upsetting the table in his hurry, anger and resentment threatening to boil over.

'Bad cess to that man. He would take the bite out of a starving child's mouth. My God, Nellie, you wouldn't consider marrying that man over me, would you?'

'I told Jimmy I would give him my answer today. No girl likes to have to wait for the man she wants till it's too late.'

'Oh, my God, Nellie, you couldn't want anything to do with Jimmy O'Driscoll.' Dan slumped back into the chair.

Nellie looks at him, the beginnings of a smile at the corners of her mouth.

'I was on my way up to meet him when you knocked on the door. It's a good job you arrived when you did, Dan Herlihy. If it wasn't for the fact that I like the name Herlihy better than I do O'Driscoll I might well have been gone long ago.'

As Dan walks the road back home, he chuckles and chortles like a man not wise. The sky is a wash of blue, from cornflower to azure, sage to purple. Muckish dominates the sweep of the bay, not even a trace of cloud shadowing its peak. On the far shore waves break against the rocky island, a frill of white surf circling the cliff base. Dan tries to guess their height, measuring them by eye, holding up his stick like a rule against the background of the brooding cliffs.

There is no one else on the road ahead of him. He turns and surveys the road behind. It too is deserted. Dan places the point of his stick firmly on the ground and dances round it, first one way, then the other.

A herd of cows placidly observes him from the far side of the hedge.

The Priest's Housekeeper

BY Pat Lawless
Loughrea, Co. Galway

*When the priest's housekeeper suddenly disappeared without a
word to anyone, the whole parish was agog. After almost running
the parish for twenty years, what could have
prompted the faithful Minnie to leave so abruptly?*

Minnie had the elusive quality of discretion. Forty-
three years old, she was Father Willie's housekeeper,
and had been for twenty or more years. He trusted
her implicitly. Almost single-handed she ran the parish. She
opened all his mail and paid all the bills. She kept the records
of births and marriages. She knew exactly whose Stations were
next. She knew who was sick in the parish and needed visiting.
Without her knowledge of the graveyard plan, bodies would
probably have been interred in the wrong graves.

She supervised the parish Ladies' Committee as they cleaned
the church each week and put fresh flowers on the altar. She
kept the record of church collections, and knew exactly who
gave what. She did the bank lodgements, and wrote letters of
thanks to donors who remembered Father Willie in their final
wills and testaments.

She knew Father Willie's signature so well that she often
signed Mass cards in his name, and no one was any the wiser.
Everything about Minnie was organised, she had a place for
everything, and everything was in its place.

Apart from her parish duties, she was the cook and washer
lady. Father Willie liked dinner at 1 p.m., unless otherwise
occupied by a funeral or wedding. So she cooked his meals and
washed his clothes, including his smalls, though never in the
same wash as her own. He liked his collars starched white, and
his black trousers neatly pressed.

As he left the house on his priestly duties, she would be standing inside the front door, with a note containing his instructions. She would hand him his black hat and a white handkerchief, brush his shoulders for dandruff, and send him on his way.

Minnie had a severe look about her. Her black hair was cut short. She never smiled, but neither did she frown. She seemed somewhere in-between. She sometimes smoked a cigarette and, if seen, would immediately apologise for it, and say, 'Don't do as I do.'

I served Mass for Father Willie for many years. During those years I observed Minnie at close quarters, and knew her well. Looking back, I like to think she had a soft spot for me, maybe because I reminded her of someone else, and she always called me 'Young Patrick.'

During those years with Father Willie, she was reluctant to accept or encourage any communication from interested men, though there were many. I knew of at least two wealthy bachelor farmers who propositioned her. Nothing untoward, just genuine offers of marriage.

It was known that she had a past - a past she did not talk about. She had been in love with an army officer. He had been only a private when they first met. His name was Oliver and he was eighteen and stood over six feet tall when Minnie saw him first. Even then he looked every inch the officer he would become.

When he was away on duty, he wrote such lovely letters, so happy, so cheerful, even when he was injured, or in dangerous places. He used to write to her about everything except the army. It was as though he was more interested in the little things they did and shared together.

When he proposed to her by letter, she was ecstatic and said yes. Her parents, who were country folk, were extremely happy for her. Minnie and her Mother planned the wedding in fine detail. They would have the cathedral for the ceremony, a guard of honour of his comrades, and a four-star hotel for the reception.

That Christmas, before the spring wedding, they spent two of the happiest weeks of their lives. They walked and talked and caught up on time lost. They went for romantic meals in the hotel. They drew up the wedding list, and even went as far as discussing table lay-out.

However, Oliver had another tour of duty before the wedding. They said their sad good-byes at Shannon Airport and vowed to write each week while they were apart. He was stationed with the United Nations peacekeepers in the Belgian Congo.

Oliver was involved in the early encounters between Africa and Europe in arenas of culture, gender and politics. He was put in charge of peacekeeping patrols in the province of Katanga where opposing tribes like the Balubas, the Bambuti and the Batwa, were tearing each other apart. This was encouraged and used as a form of terrorism by Belgium in an effort to avoid Congo independence, because the Congo had rubber trees, and rubber was a valuable and expensive commodity.

When the Balubas attacked Oliver's patrol, nine men of the patrol were killed. One of them was Oliver.

A few weeks later, his hometown came to a standstill when his remains were brought there in a sealed coffin. He was buried with full military honours. All the dignitaries were there, and the President and Government were represented.

With so many people around and so many sympathisers, Minnie had no time to grieve on her own.

'We're there if you need us.'

'Don't be alone, call us.'

'So sorry for your loss.'

Oliver's parents were shattered. Their only child dead! Minnie tried to comfort them as best she could, and it brought them close for a while. However, reality soon struck home.

Minnie was pregnant.

When the lady doctor confirmed the news, Minnie fidgeted in her chair and there was a silence, a long silence. Minnie it was who seemed first conscious of the need for communication, and she reassured the doctor that everything would be fine.

'Will you marry this young man?' enquired the doctor.

'I would love to,' Minnie replied.

She then put her hand to her mouth, and whispered almost inaudibly; 'No.'

She blurted out the reason, and unloaded her pent-up sorrow on the doctor.

'Where was your boy killed,' the doctor asked.

Minnie stared at the ground in silence before answering.

'That dreadful fighting,' she said. 'Why do they do it?'

'Where was your boy killed?' the doctor repeated.

After a long pause Minnie replied, 'He had deep blue eyes, dark hair, and was tall and strong. He wrote the loveliest letters and poetry, and he stood out in any crowd.'

On 21st September the baby boy was born. Minnie christened him Oliver, after his dad. She suffered severe post-natal depression, and spent a time in a home for unmarried mothers. She signed adoption papers and Oliver was taken from her at eleven months.

Minnie was never her old self again. She became withdrawn and distant. Her parents were affected by her behaviour and worried about her so much that little else occupied their minds. Minnie spent long periods alone in her room, and appeared to shun any kind of company.

Her parents asked their Parish Priest, Father Willie, to come to the house to talk to Minnie. He did, and after much cajoling, Minnie agreed to go to his house to help him sort out some paperwork. By natural progression, and because she enjoyed it, Minnie took on the position of priest's housekeeper, and moved into her own quarters in the parochial house.

Now, twenty years on, Minnie was indispensable to Father Willie. Her parents had passed away and any contact she had with her extended family was miniscule.

When Minnie disappeared that September, to say it was surprising would be a huge understatement. The neighbours and parishioners failed to throw any light on her whereabouts. Or on why she had so suddenly disappeared. Nothing had indicated that she'd been on the verge of leaving. She left one night without a word to anyone.

Father Willie thought he heard the floorboards on the landing of the old parochial house creaking. He opened the door inch by inch and stepped quietly into the landing. He saw nothing.

Within hours of her disappearance, Father Willie began to panic. All Minnie's clothes and personal belongings other than some old shoes, were gone. At first the flustered priest couldn't find his appointments book or diary, but when he calmed down he found everything in its correct place, including a note apologising for the abrupt departure.

The first Mass by Father Willie on the following Sunday was packed, even though it was at 8 o' clock and usually had a small crowd. Word had spread around the parish that something had happened. In his homily, Father Willie spoke of his hurt and disappointment at Minnie's sudden disappearance, at the same time acknowledging all the great work she had done for him and the parish

For a few weeks little else was talked about in the parish; Minnie's disappearance became a village tale for the ear of every stranger. The parishioners speculated among themselves about whether anything untoward had occurred between the priest and his housekeeper. There was also a rumour of missing parish funds, though this was never substantiated. The rumours eventually died down as Father Willie continued to minister, and his parish flourished as life moved on.

I often wondered what became of Minnie. I like to think she had a plan.

Maybe she had a lover. Was he a married man? Perhaps she had traced her son, and went to live near him in another part of the country?

Or had she grown bitter with the church? After all, she had spent some time in a home run by nuns. It was where she had given up her son for adoption. Was she forced into this?

Whatever her reason for disappearing, no trace of Minnie was ever found, despite extensive searches. However, she was never added to the missing person's register.

There the story might have ended - but it didn't.

Some years ago, my son Dylan and friends hired a six-berth River Cruiser in Portumna. They had decided to holiday in Ireland. They travelled the Shannon River, heading upstream for ten or so days. Each day they would berth in different towns and sample the delights on offer.

On Sunday my wife and I decided to meet them in Carrick-on-Shannon for Sunday lunch and a trip on their cruiser. We got there early.

The place was packed with people, and we walked the prom, arm in arm, looking downriver awaiting the arrival of Dylan and friends. We sat for a break on a long bench seat by the river, not taking any notice of who we had sat beside.

'Young Patrick, is that you?' I heard someone say.

I looked at the old lady sitting beside us. She was staring at me.

'You have me at a disadvantage,' I said.

'You don't remember me, do you?' she said.

'Should I?' I replied.

'My name is Minnie,' she said. 'And you were the same age as my son, that's why I remember you, and you haven't really changed.'

It all came flooding back to me-the priest's housekeeper, the death of a young army officer, the disappearance, the mystery!

We talked for a long while, as Minnie seemed keen to tell me her story.

An Irish family living in County Leitrim had adopted her son. They had since died, and he had inherited the thriving family business. Only when both his parents had passed away had he found out that he was adopted.

From then on he tried every known way to find out if his birth parents were still alive. He met obstacle after obstacle as the authorities gave little assistance in his search.

Eventually, through chance, after almost all agencies had failed to provide any answers, the Galway Magdalen home for unmarried mothers found his file.

Following contact through an intermediary, a meeting was set up for Minnie to meet her long-lost son.

The meeting went very well, as both parties were very keen to make up for lost time. Oliver looked just like his dad and he was very happy to have photos and other clippings and writings about his father.

Minnie said that although she had been the priest's housekeeper for many years, she felt that her own life was private.

So, when her son insisted that she come and live with him and his wife and her grandchildren, she eventually relented.

'I am finally at peace,' she said.

As she walked away, she was holding the hand of a young boy who was her great grandchild, her third in total.

I looked at my wife, thinking of what Minnie had told me and what she had called me. 'Young Patrick,' I said, and squeezed her hand.

The Other Curly Campbell

A *memory by* Gabrielle Nelson

Roscommon

A local tough guy shows another side to his character with an Elvis rendition.

I was 16 years old and working at my summer job in a café in a Southern seaside town. It was eight o'clock in the morning and my turn to get up early. I wasn't fully awake.

The night before had been pretty hectic with running street battles between rival gangs that had spilled over into the café. I was used to seeing skirmishes on the street but it was my first time to see flying saucers and cups and teapots.

The main gang was headed by a big guy called Curly Campbell. With his shaven head and burly physique he had a reputation for violence. Very few people encroached on his turf and those who did, found themselves with broken limbs or concussion. It was like West Side Story meets the Wild West. Curly and his gang often hung around the jukebox in our café playing records, drinking coke and planning the next turf war. Most of the locals held him in a mixture of awe and terror.

This morning I was busy setting the tables in readiness for any early morning customers who happened to drop in.

I didn't hear the door open so it was quite a shock to look up into the face of a very grim Curly who was alone and bearing many battle scars. I thought it wiser not to mention the fact that he had been barred because of his antics the previous night.

He ordered a full breakfast and it was difficult frying rashers and sausages and keeping an eye on him in case he wrecked the place. He ate his meal in silence then walked over to the jukebox, unplugged it and pushed it out from the wall. At this stage I was calculating how many minutes it would take me to run upstairs and wake Antonio, the café owner. I was convinced he was going to smash the records that were banked under the glass dome. Instead, he lowered his large frame until he was peering out at me through the glass above the records.

To my astonishment he launched into 'Wooden Heart'.

'Treat me nice, treat me good,

Treat me like you really should'.

He had the soft, gentle voice of the King himself. If I had dared close my eyes I could have sworn that Elvis had dropped by.

'Cos I'm not made of wood, and I don't have a wooden heart'.

Well, who would believe that? When the last words trilled away he came out, re-plugged the jukebox, threw the money for the breakfast on the counter and walked out.

When I told Antonio later he reprimanded me for not barring him. I'm glad I didn't. At least I caught a glimpse of the real Curly Campbell.

Travellers

Joe Spearin
Clonlara, Co. Clare

A chance meeting during a plane journey caused Ted Ross to make dramatic changes in his retirement plans.

The plane rolling slowly towards the holding point of runway 31 left at JFK International Airport was an Airbus A330. Aesthetically beautiful in its design, its stylish livery gave an added touch of class to its appearance. The low whining of its huge engines belied their potential power. Inside the cabin the passengers were being coached on the safety procedures by the flight attendants.

As the plane turned to line up on the runway, the seat-belt signs illuminated and a hush spread throughout the cabin. They were ready for take-off. This was the part that Ted Ross liked the best. The noise from the engines rose to a crescendo and, with the brakes disengaged, the plane began to move forward, slowly at first, but soon it was thundering along, increasing in speed until it achieved the buoyancy necessary to lift itself into the air.

This was the moment when Ted always felt the exhilaration he was sure the Wright brothers must have felt at Kitty Hawk when their primitive flying machine first lifted off the ground.

At 500 feet, the Airbus began a slow left-hand turn and, with its landing gear retracted, it gained height rapidly. Its course would take it along the east coast of North America towards Newfoundland and then out across the Atlantic Ocean.

The quietness that abounded throughout the cabin during take-off was replaced by chatter as passengers relaxed and settled down for the long flight ahead. Ted could understand that not everybody enjoyed travelling by air as much as he did. He had often seen parents who might themselves be jittery trying to cajole and coax reluctant children onto a plane.

Flight attendants were brilliant in situations like that and Ted had often admired their ability to put people at their ease. Travelling by air was an unfamiliar experience for some individuals and special skills were needed to help them adjust to their environment. Along with answering queries, they served food, sold merchandise and ensured that every flight was as pleasant an experience as possible for each passenger.

The Airbus was still gaining height and, at three thousand feet, those passengers with window seats could see wispy patches of cloud swirling by outside. They would soon be high above the weather where there would be clear air and sunshine.

Ted had noticed, as boarding was taking place, that quite a few entering the cabin were regular travellers on the route. He had seen them time and again when he had been going home himself. Some of the cabin crew were familiar to him as well. He would miss them, he thought. Today's flight was his last. He was going home to stay this time.

He had reached retiring age and the company he had worked with for more than thirty years was letting him go. He would gladly have continued on, but it was all down to rules and regulations. Mid-fifties seemed a bit early to be calling it a day, but he had reached the milestone and a generous retirement package would soften the impact of having to leave the workplace behind.

The engines of the plane assumed a quieter note as it reached its cruising altitude. With the help of the Gulf Stream tailwind, its progress would be swift and smooth. An announcement told passengers that the weather in Dublin, their destination, was dry and sunny.

Ted glanced across at the young man sitting alongside him. This clean-cut chap reminded him of what he, himself, looked like twenty odd years ago. Funny how time passes so quickly, he thought. In those days he had had plans to settle down and raise a family, but there never seemed to be the right moment to make that move. His career always got in the way. Relationships with potential partners were doomed to fail as he was never at home for more than a few days at a time. Girls looked for stability. They wanted their boyfriends to be close by. Someone who flitted from place to place all the time did not appeal to many of them.

A year ago, and, with the thoughts of his impending retirement going through his mind, he had wondered what he might do to keep himself occupied. The old empty house on the north side of Dublin that he stayed in whenever he was at home needed refurbishment.

It had been bequeathed to him by his late parents but he never had the time or inclination to look after it properly. Yes, he thought, he would make a start on it, redecorate it, buy new furniture, paint the outside, re-set the garden.

It was at that time, too, on a day when he was pondering on his future, that he had first encountered Wendy. Wendy was a flight attendant, new to the route on which he was travelling now. She was tall, dark-haired and she had the most captivating smile he had ever seen. It lit up her face and made her eyes sparkle. She wore very little make-up. She didn't need it. She was on in-flight catering duty on that day.

Placing her tray of refreshments alongside him, she asked him his preference. 'Black coffee and digestive biscuits please,' he said. He watched as her slender hands put the items down in front of him.

'If there's anything else you need, just give me a shout,' she purred, her smiling eyes flashing as she spoke. He called her shortly afterwards asking for more coffee and biscuits, not because he was still hungry , but because he wanted to have some contact with her again. And it was magic!

This time she came close enough for him to detect the delicate fragrance of expensive perfume, bought perhaps on a recent stopover in London or Paris. She was young enough to be his daughter, but her self-assurance and confident manner showed a maturity that was impressive.

Love at first sight was something he had read about in novels and he had often wondered what it might be like. As she moved away, he turned to watch her and, with a backward glance, she caught him. Again she smiled that smile. He dunked a biscuit and left it for too long in the coffee so that most of it sank. He put it down to distraction and wondered what kind of foolishness was going on inside his head. Had there been some spark, some chemistry at work here or were his fanciful thoughts just the idle dreamings of a middle-aged romantic? He knew that altitude sickness came in many different forms, and he wondered if there might be a Cupid's Arrow variety of the malady.

He saw her again later on in the day, after they landed in Dublin. She was making her way through the concourse dragging one of those wheeled luggage carriers, trademark accessory of all air hostesses.

'Hello again,' he greeted her. 'Heading for home I suppose.'

'No,' she replied, 'my home is in Connemara, too far away. I'm on an early flight to London in the morning so it has to be the hotel for me tonight.'

He asked her which hotel she was heading for and then offered to drive her there, an offer she accepted.

'Would you like a drink,' she asked when they reached their destination, adding with a smile, 'in the bar that is.'

She drank beer shandy while he settled for regular coke. She was a good talker and she made him laugh with tales of being stranded in exotic places when there were foul-ups in schedules.

She showed great interest in his love of travel and she was genuinely saddened to learn of his impending retirement. 'No,' she didn't have a partner, 'never met anyone yet who stirred my emotions' was how she put it, and he pondered on her use of the word 'yet'.

'House on fire' would have been the clichéd term to describe how they got on together in the short time they spent in the bar that evening and it was with reluctance that he bade her goodnight just after ten o'clock, mindful of her early start in the morning.

His itinerary in the following weeks had him commuting between Chicago and Los Angeles and it wasn't until he was on the homeward trip to Dublin that he saw her again. She was visibly pleased to see him and, after they had landed, he took her to one of the quieter inner-city pubs where they had soup and meat sandwiches and where they talked until it was near to closing time. She stayed the night with him in his north side house. He made no excuse for its unkempt condition and she didn't comment on the dust that covered the furniture.

Their meetings became more frequent, not only in Dublin, but wherever their schedules put them in the same place at the same time. They met in New York, Boston and Chicago. Totally smitten by her allure and charm, he was chuffed to have her by his side in restaurants, cinemas and theatres. She, for her part, saw him as a handsome escort, his greying hair adding a distinguished look to his appearance. He was debonair and chivalrous, a thorough gentleman, she thought.

There was one thing about him that surprised her and that was his shyness when it came to talking about his work.

'Leave the job behind at the end of each day' was his motto. People who went on and on about their occupations bored him. On a weekend break in Orlando, she saw him deflect the attentions of an inquisitive barman who had asked him what line of business he was in.

'I travel a lot,' was Ted's reply and, before the man could probe any further, he added, 'but then aren't we all travellers of some sort in this world as we make our journey through life?'

As the Airbus continued to make steady progress, Ted reflected on his own life's journey during the past year. Meeting Wendy had made the spectre of his impending retirement seem almost irrelevant. She had given him a sense of purpose, a new outlook and a desire to embrace whatever the future might hold.

She put him off the idea of redecorating the house. 'That can wait until sometime later,' she told him. She booked a boating holiday on the river Shannon so that he could relax in the first weeks of his retirement. It would be a perfect beginning, she thought, to a more leisurely lifestyle for the man she had fallen in love with.

'The usual, I suppose.' His reverie was interrupted by Wendy's voice as she stood beside him with her trolley. 'Black coffee and digestives,' they both spoke in unison and the young man sitting next to Ted smiled.

As the Airbus reached the Irish coast, the engines assumed a quieter tone as the power eased off. A thick blanket of low-lying cloud obscured the landscape beneath. This cloud would break up as they went further inland. An announcement from the cockpit telling passengers that they were beginning their descent gave rise to murmurs of anticipation.

The sky was almost cloudless now and the countryside below looked magnificent in its pastoral splendour, the patterned blanket of fields and foliage blending into a rich tapestry of natural beauty.

Familiar landmarks were identified by some people while others tried to guess the names of towns and villages as they passed beneath. The plane began to make a long, sweeping turn, levelling out as it lined up with the runway which was still a good distance away. Flaps and undercarriage were lowered, slowing the Airbus down a little more. They were floating gently now, the engines almost sighing as they crossed the threshold of the runway. Puffs of white smoke came from where the tyres made contact with the tarmac, the nose wheel being the last to touch the ground. They were landed.

As the passengers began to disembark, the flight attendants went to work checking the interior of the plane. Wendy took up a position at the main exit. She smiled and exchanged words of farewell to those she recognised as regular commuters. When the cabin was empty she pressed the coded panel on the cockpit door and when it opened, the first to emerge was the young clean-cut co-pilot. He was followed by captain Ted Ross. Wendy accompanied both men into the terminal building, pausing for just a moment while Ted turned to catch a last glimpse of his beloved aircraft.

The Widda's Answer

By Phil Cassidy

Smithboro, Co. Monaghan

Lena smiled proudly as she watched Bobby striding down the lane.
He was a fine cut of man and she had a feeling that he would be
well received by the widow.

'Will you go and axe the Widda the day?' Dinny asked as he cut the top off his boiled egg and sprinkled it with a liberal helping of salt.

'Ask her, not axe her.' His sister Lena corrected, pouring herself a cup of tea.

'What are you buttin' your nose in for, I'll talk the way I've always talked.' He glowered at her across the table.

'Now,' he said, turning his attention back to his younger brother Bobby, 'will you axe her the day or not?'

Bobby didn't answer, just concentrated on spreading a large chunk of butter on a thick slice of toast.

'Are you deaf or what? For the love of God, will you do it or not?'

'I suppose I'll have to, or you'll not stop harping until I do.'

Lena smiled at her younger brother, glad that he'd agreed to go for the sake of peace. She felt sorry for him, Dinny bullied him non-stop. She wished he'd gone to America like the other brothers and made a life for himself. But Dinny had always suffered poor health because of his bad chest, so somehow their parents had managed to hold on to him as well as herself. Her chances of changing her life were long gone as she would be turning sixty next month, but Bobby could still do something to get away from the old grump. He was in his early forties and she dreamed of seeing him happy in his own corner.

'Get a move on if you're going, or it'll soon be dinner time.'

'Leave him alone and let him finish his breakfast. Anyway, he'll have to shave and put on his good clothes, show the widow a bit of respect,' Lena piped up.

'Ach, would you whist and stop treating him like a wee boy. I'll not always be around to guide him.'

'Ach, whist yourself, if grumpy old men were scarce you'd make a half a dozen.'

Dinny snorted and, scraping his chair back, rose slowly and shuffled across the kitchen towards the back door.

Half an hour later, Bobby was ready to go. Lena smiled proudly as she watched him striding down the lane. He was a fine cut of a man with his broad shoulders and head of reddish brown curly hair.

She busied herself doing her chores, all the while hoping the widow would take kindly to Bobby. When the dishes were washed, floor swept, hens fed and clothes left soaking in the big tin bath, she got the bag of hay she used as a cushion when weeding in her beloved garden. It was the one place she felt at peace and time went quickly. She dead-headed the roses, leaving the yellow climbing one to last as she always did because it was her favourite. It had been growing around the trunk of the big copper beech for nearly forty years.

She could remember as clear as yesterday the day the she had planted it. Even after all these years it still brought a smile to her face although it was tinged with a little sadness. It had been a present for her birthday and she'd had to practically plant it in the dark because if her father or Dinnny had found it, they would have destroyed it. They had not approved of her boyfriend, not good enough because his family had no land. She inhaled the sweet scent of the rose and stood gazing across the valley lost in a happy memory from long ago.

'What the hell's keeping him anyway, I only wanted him to axe her, not move in with her.'

The peace was broken by the sound of Dinny's gruff voice.

Lena sighed, she'd better go and make him a mug of tea or he'd stand there complaining until she did.

'Sure he's just being polite. You couldn't expect him to knock on the door, ask her and then turn on his heel and march away.'

'I would have, just do the business and go, that's always been my way.'

'Aye, and look how far that got you.' Lena muttered to herself.

Just as she sat down to drink her tea, she heard the rattle of the latch as the back door opened and Bobby came in, red faced and smiling.

Lena jumped to her feet, two little pink spots of excitement colouring her cheeks.

'Well,' she asked, eyes shining.'

'She's a very nice woman, a handsome woman. She made me tea and buns, lovely buns with cream and jam and two little wings on top.'

'Ach, would you quit blathering and tell us what she said?' Dinny was impatient to know the answer. 'And I'd know from the big red head on you she gave you more than tea and buns.'

'She surely did, she gave me two glasses of the finest whiskey I've ever tasted and then she said yes.' He nodded his head to emphasise the importance of that word.

'She said yes, we could have the loan of her wheelbarrow any time we needed it.'

MICK NEILL'S DAUGHTER

A MEMORY BY JOAN CLEERE
Bennettsbridge, Co. Kilkenny

Remembering a loving father and happy childhood days growing up in Thomastown.

I can still see him standing at The Gap, a local fishing spot in Thomastown, casting his line into the surging water - a man who loved the river bank and who would spend hours waiting for the salmon to bite. Many times I was there when a tug would come on the line and my heart would nearly stop with excitement. My father would play the fish up and down, reeling it in slowly and carefully and then he would produce the gaff to kill the fish.

When it was on the bank, he would take a piece of twine from his pocket. This he would thread through a little wooden handle and the fish would be tied at the mouth and the tail making a half-moon shape that was then carried like a bucket. I often carried the salmon proudly through the town to Crennan's shop where it would be weighed, and the weight taken note of until later, when my father would call for the money.

When I was a child I spent hours at the river with him after school. I would call into the chemist's shop to buy a stick of barley sugar or blackjack to take to him. We never spoke a lot as I recall, but I was content just to be there. He made all his own weights and flies. This operation was one that my brother and I watched with interest.

He had moulds fashioned from hard-wall that he had made with matchboxes. In the middle of the two moulds he would scrape out a circular shape - he would then tie the two pieces together with the holes meeting. The next step was to take the boiling lead that had been heating over the fire in an old can kept specially for this purpose. He would then pour the lead carefully through a small opening he had made earlier.

During the shooting season, the smell of pheasant cooking was a familiar one in our house. To this day I can recall the smell of burning feathers after the plucking operation. We used to fight over who would help my father to clean his gun. He had a little brush on the end of a string and he would put it down the barrel of the gun to clean it and we would pull it out the other end.

We always had a succession of dogs in our house and the name that cropped up most often was 'Grouse.' My father's love of shooting and fishing was passed on to my brother who is a keen sportsman.

The local flour mill provided a lot of the employment at the time and my father worked there as a lorry helper and in the mill itself. In later years the dust in the mill was to take its toll on his health. Often, I called to see him at the mill. We passed it on our way to pick blackberries and sometimes we would see him looking out through one of the little windows and he would call us in.

The workings of the mill held a fascination for us and the noise and the thumping of the machinery would vibrate the ground under us.

To the left of the mill-yard, in a little shed, an important job was carried out. Several women would be seated here sewing bags. They were called 'bag women' and they used huge needles for their work. One of the women was a very jolly person. Her name was Roundy and she always had a word for us.

The women wore big sacks tied in apron fashion around their waists. Sometimes, when my father was helping on the lorries, he would have to go to Dublin and when this happened, we looked out for him coming home as he always brought us a stick of rock.

The mill played an important part in our lives and when it ceased production, many of the workers received large sums of money in compensation. Unfortunately, my father was out sick at this time and was not awarded any money. So, after his years of loyal service he got nothing. He felt this keenly at the time, particularly as his health wasn't good.

Some Sunday afternoons we would go for a walk up the Rock Road with my mother and father. These were simple pleasures. We would pick frauchans and wild strawberries in the nearby woods. Sometimes we would meet friends of my father's. One such character was 'Bargy,' an old and wizened man with a rather frog-like appearance. There was always time to chat.

Other trips with my father included outings to Kilkenny on the train to hurling matches. He was a great follower of the G.A,A. and was a hurler of some note himself, having played with Thomastown and also with a London team.

A big event in our house was the day the wireless arrived. We stood and looked in awe at this box that was placed on the press in the corner. It was a source of great entertainment for us, and I recall vividly programmes which we followed faithfully each week, such as Dan Dare and Digby, Take Your Pick, Double Your Money and many more.

As we got older, my brother and I would tune into Radio Luxembourg for the latest hits. My parents and younger sister would be in bed and, at the height of the programme, there would be a thump on the floor and a shout from my father telling us to 'Go to bed out of that' or 'are ye going to stay up all night?'

My father enjoyed his pint and usually went out three or four nights a week. At one stage, I remember, I used to sleep on a small bed in my parents' room and I would be half awake when he would arrive home from the pub. He would relate the happenings of the evening to my mother and tell her who had 'stood' him a pint. He would empty his pockets on the small table beside the bed.

On nights when he didn't go to the pub, I would be sent for a baby Power and two small bottles of Guinness. He had a lovely singing voice and his favourite song was 'Thora', followed closely by 'I'll take you home again Kathleen.'

I only once saw him cry and that was the night they carried my mother down the stairs on a stretcher to take her to hospital. My young sister was only a few weeks old at the time and in later years, I understood how he felt. My mother spent thirteen weeks in hospital with pleurisy, but, thankfully, made a full recovery.

I recall a funny incident that he used to relate to my intense embarrassment. This involved a certain publican in the town who used to go for walks in the country on his day off. He always carried a bag of three-penny bits (the old bronze type) and he would distribute them to children as he met them on the road. Needless to say, being children, we loved to meet him and, to be honest, it wouldn't always be an accidental meeting.

Anyway on this particular day, I met him and he produced the bag asking me who I was and I replied, 'I'm Mick Neill's daughter,' probably thinking that this information might be worth another three-penny bit. Of course, he must have told my father about it.

In his younger days, my father was a member of the old I.R.A, and he spent some time on the run when the Black and Tans were in Ireland. He was the holder of an I.R.A. medal and was later awarded a pension in recognition of his service.

In the late fifties, his health deteriorated and he had a serious operation. As a result, he had breathing difficulties. I often saw him after that sitting on a window-sill halfway up Maudlin (the hill leading to the terrace where we lived) to get his breath back. I wonder did he set himself this target at the bottom of the hill?

My father died on the 21st of December, 1963, at the age of 62. What a waste, he never lived to see any of his grandchildren and we never had the opportunity to get to know him as young adults. I like to think that he would have been content at the way our lives have turned out and, after all this time, I'm still proud to tell people 'I'm Mick Neill's daughter.'

WRITING A CHRISTMAS STORY

By JAMES FAIRHURST
Wigan, England

*We were lying on the sand when the subject of writing a story
reared its head. I was drowsy with wine, totally relaxed. 'Just to
please me,' she coaxed. 'I'll be satisfied if you'll just try once.'*

Although we got to know each other at a local writers'
club we knew each other by sight, for quite often we
had been in the library at the same time, and the fact
that we were both readers was an instant bond. Fiction was her
constant study and she had had several short stories published.
Detective novels were a passion and she claimed to read two a
week. I preferred reality for, to me, the true story was the only
tale worth telling.

The local newspaper had accepted several of my articles,
and the features editor assured me he would always welcome
more of the same. She read them with mild interest, but it
was obvious they were not for her. An article I wrote about a
nineteenth century murder trial, its conviction and aftermath
started suggestions that became more and more frequent.

'Have you never thought what a good story that would
make,' she said when we were having drinks after the writers'
meeting was over. 'You don't have to keep to the facts. You
can use them to embroider the story, to make it longer and
more complex.'

At that moment, I was satisfied with the cheque I had just
received and was happy to continue as I was. Once a week, I
would book a reader at the town's History Shop and look over
past editions of local newspapers that were on microfilm.

At each sitting I usually got a couple of stories that needed
a little re-arranging and editing. I learned as I went along. If
an article was rejected, I was soon able to see why and amend
succeeding pieces accordingly. Now and then, the features

editor might advise as to what was and was not acceptable. I had looked at several magazines and noticed there were far more articles published than short stories. In addition and as time passed, ideas came more easily and seemed to be hiding around every corner.

My friend was hard to convince. 'All I am asking,' she insisted, 'is that you give it a try. I'm sure you would be good at it. You write well and you should make the most of your writing.' The discussion would end as it usually did with my promising to keep it in mind, only to be revived when one of her stories appeared in print.

This apart, we did get on well with each other. We enjoyed dancing, we had dinner once a week, and sometimes I even read a book she suggested although I had no time for detective fiction. I had read all the Conan Doyle and Agatha Christie stories and felt that later detective mysteries were only derived from these.

However, summer was almost upon us and thoughts of a holiday occupied our minds. She waxed lyrical over the prospects of hot golden sands, calm, deep blue seas and long summer nights when the world seemed to have stopped breathing.

'Think,' she dreamed, 'How enchanting it would be to sail away from England's indifferent climate and go southwards to some island paradise where, minimally dressed we could laze beneath tropical palms. How restful it would be during the day to stroll through small villages charmed by the natives in their colourful reds and greens bedecking their brown bodies. How soothing to walk hand in hand along sun-kissed beaches, to sit, side by side, in the evening, gossiping with other visitors, sipping sparkling wine as the setting sun tinged everything with yellow and gold, to spend each night sleeping under a single sheet and to awaken at dawn to a silence so profound that we only spoke in whispers'.

I soon put a stop to that dream. 'We're going to Sitges in Spain, a place where I can find some booze.' And as an afterthought I added, 'And before August sets in with its usual severity'.

So it turned out. We made friends with the English people also staying at the Hotel Sonrisa and quickly found a place owned by Londoners who could give us a full English breakfast instead of the usual coffee and rolls. For the only time in our lives, we watched a bullfight, having been conned into it by the courier who argued persuasively that 'Coming to Spain and not seeing a bullfight is like visiting Rome and not seeing the Pope.'

I thought of the possibility of an article until remembering that Hemmingway had exhausted that topic. We were lying on the sands when the holiday was coming to its close when the subject of writing raised its head. I was drowsy with wine, totally relaxed, easy prey.'

Just to please me,' she coaxed. 'I'll be satisfied if you'll just try once.'

To get the matter out of the way, to consign it to a far-off period, I remarked, off-handedly in a moment of weakness: 'Well, I've always wanted to write a Christmas story'.

After that, there was no getting out of it. It is amazing how time flies for we had hardly returned from holiday it seemed before October was here. She had no intention of letting the matter drop.

'Magazines need about six week's grace,' she informed me, 'so you should have your piece ready by early November.'

I always write my articles in long-hand being one of those strange creatures who actually likes writing with a pen. I like to make my mistakes first so the piece might be rewritten several times before being typed. With hardly an idea in mind and wishing only to keep the peace, I began:

'The Christmas tree dominated the village square, its red and green fairy lights casting a warm glow over the fallen snow. Church bells had begun their low, melodious din, calling the faithful to Midnight Mass. Of all the good times in the year it was Christmas Eve and the world was at peace.'

At this point, I sensed she was peering over my shoulder so I put down my pen and turned around. I was conscious at once of the pained expression on her face.

'You don't like it?' I queried. She was silent for a moment and then, choosing her words carefully, she muttered: 'It's .....It's well if you must know, it's so ordinary. There isn't an original word in the whole paragraph.'

'It's only the beginning', I protested.

'The beginning is the most important thing,' she said.

'The first paragraph should never be ordinary. You have to grab the reader at the start, making them want to read on. No one would want to read the rest of that pap.'

'Tell me, then,' I said, 'how should I have started?'

'Well,' she replied, 'had you begun by saying that the Christmas tree lay in ruins, its lights smashed with its glass littering the floor, you'd be on my wavelength. I'd say at once, 'vandalism' and want to know what came next.'

Again I protested: 'But I was setting the scene, a scene of peace. I didn't mean it to be about violence.'

'What would it have been about then?'

'Well, to be truthful, I hadn't decided. I was hoping to get some inspiration from writing.'

'That's another mistake,' she insisted. 'You can't plot well if you don't plan well. And since you began with the Christmas tree, it will have to figure somewhere in the rest of the story.'

'I hadn't thought of that.'

'Think of it now. And look at that line: 'Of all the good times in the year it was Christmas Eve.' 'You've got that from Dickens. It is in his Christmas Carol.'

'Did I? I wasn't conscious of it.'

'It's called unconscious remembering. It happens to the best writers not only sentences, but plots as well.' They stick in the mind and, later on, writers believe them to be their own.'

'I think, then, I should leave Christmas writing to Charles Dickens.'

'Oh no, he wrote about what he knew in his day. Write about what you feel strongly about now...then look at that last line. 'The world was at peace. Has the world ever been at peace?'

'There has never been and there never will be a time when the world will be at peace. Why not start again?'

Half an hour later she looked over my shoulder and read: 'The police car drew up beside the wrecked Christmas tree on the village square. The broken glass of the fairy lights crunched beneath the police sergeant's feet as he circled the damaged symbol of the approaching festivities. A strange silence hung in the air.'

'That's more promising,' she said., 'and more up to date. What's the strange silence about?'

'No bells,' I said. 'They've been nicked. I was going to put that the yelps of the carol singers filled the air as they were being mugged, but that was perhaps coming it a bit strong.'

Her eyes narrowed showing disbelief and her eyebrows were raised in puzzled interrogation.

'Are you having me on?'

'No, no,' I said. 'And notice the first thing I mentioned was the police car and the sergeant. My story will be about him and how he spends his Christmas. He's sickened by violence and when he gets home, his supper's cold and his wife's been to a party and only comes in later. In his rage, he slaps her face. If the surgery had been open on Christmas Day she'd have gone to the doctor to show him the bruise that would be evidence for divorce.'

'You really are taking the Mick,' she said.

'Let me read you some more. Their daughter is pregnant and doesn't know who the father is. Their son, still at school, is on drugs. On Christmas Day, they get the news that their parents, whom they've neglected for years, have been taken to hospital with hypothermia. If Dickens were alive today he'd have a field day.'

She regarded me coldly.

'I'm going to do some Christmas shopping, are you coming?'

INTERNED

A MEMORY BY SUSAN CONDON
Kingswood Heights, Dublin

*The discovery of a bundle of letters reveals what life was like in
Ballykinlar camp during the War of Independance*

Eighty-year-old Jim received a call from his older sister,
Monica, asking if he could repair the old piano in the
parlour of their family home. It was there, hidden inside,
that he discovered the bundle of letters. He opened twined knots
to release a dozen off-white faded and torn envelopes. Each had
a two-penny stamp pasted in the top right corner, the address
beautifully penned in fading black ink.

Each was written by his father, John, and sent to his mother
during the war for Irish independence, dating from 1921 to
1923, while he was interned in Ballykinlar Prison Camp, in
County Down.

Their formal air spoke of different times, each signed off
with 'best of love to all at home, from your loving son, John,'
with references to 'Father' and addressed to 'Dear Mother.'
'Rounded up and taken' along with many others to Wellington
Barracks on

1st December, 1920, John had scribbled notes on scraps of
paper, telling his mother that he was okay. He expected to be
released soon, as he had 'never mixed up in any party' and asked
if she could bring a collar and handkerchief for his release.

Mother had spoken to a lieutenant at the barracks and he had
promised to see what could be done. A meeting with O'Neill &
Collins, solicitors, in North Brunswick Street had been arranged
for 11th December, 1920.

In October, 1921, letters from John were arriving - now from
Ballykinlar Prison Camp. They revealed what the daily routine
in the camp was like.

They rose at 7.30 a.m., eventually retiring at 9.00 p.m. when they would make Bovril, then recite the rosary and go to bed at 9.45 p.m. Papers delivered to the camp could be bought for two bob. Camp rules allowed prisoners to post no more than two letters per week, of no more than two pages in length, and both had to be sent in the same envelope. Most letters were written on Sunday and were four pages long.

Parcels from home would be shared around. No eggs, but supplies of butter, tea leaves, fruit cake, cigarettes and strings could be sent. Apparently, one of his fellow interns was Martin Walton, who formed the camp orchestra and taught them to play the violin. He was yet to found the famous Walton's Music Shop and the Walton's music programme which always finished with the words: 'If you feel like singing, do sing an Irish song.' Other internees included Peadar Kearney, co-author of the national anthem, and Sean Lemass who, in 1959, would succeed Eamonn De Valera as Taoiseach.

John requested a kit-bag from home so that, like the four chaps he shared with, he could use it to store his clothes neatly. He frequently requested pencils and colours.

Among the letters were sketches he had made from Hut 29. Barbed wire covered the windows outside. Blankets and sheets were piled neatly on low wooden cots. Small shelves were set high on walls – milk and Lipton's tea sitting atop one; a small selection of papers and books lay flat on another, beneath a chess set. Pegs were set into the wall and held coats and hats.

Other sketches showed a row of rust-coloured huts running down the camp, a dark mountain looming in the background, echoing the atmosphere. Another showed 'The Altar, Ballykinlar.' Music notes for 'Show a leg' appeared on another page along with a pattern for a suit jacket on the back.

The last showed a hut with two crosses, one on either side of the door. The words 'Where Sloan and Tormey Died,' were written beneath and it was dated 17th Jan., 1921.

Sports Day arranged for 17th March, 1921 - St Patrick's Day – had not been a success due to the weather. 'I hope the weather is better in old Dublin, it is wild here, but dry and the sand would cut the eyes out of your head. Talk about the sands of the desert,' he'd written. They had, however, enjoyed a concert that night.

On 7th August, 1921, he mentioned rumours that they might soon be returning home but that he would never forget 1st December, 1920.

'I think this will be a different winter. I'll not forget the 1st of Dec., 1920, in all my life. I don't suppose any of you will at home. I have a good laugh at it by times, when I think of Father with the blanket round him. I don't expect he will forget it in a hurry. Does he laugh over it? I don't think so, but I will make him laugh over my times since, even though they are not all laughable ones I may tell you.'

In the final letter, John was looking forward to returning home and back to his job as a tailor/cutter with Messrs. Scotts. He asked his mother to be sure that his blue suit would be ready for him to go 'clicking.'

Under The Bridge

Sandra Harris

Cuffe Street, Dublin

*Rain or shine, it makes no odds to Molly, though when the winter
snow is at its deepest and sleeping under the bridge is impossible,
she will take herself off to the Homeless Shelter in
the centre of town.*

Splat! The moth-eaten tennis ball hits Molly squarely
on the back of the head. The grey woolly hat she wears
winter and summer alike cushions her head from any ill-
effects, though the blow constitutes a mild irritation rather than
anything approximating real pain.

'Feck off, ye little brats!' Molly roars as she turns and makes
as if to charge her shopping trolley right into the ranks of
jeering, laughing teenage boys. The boys scatter, lobbing insults
like 'Crazy old bag lady!' when they are a safe distance away.

Molly carries on unhurriedly up the road. She doesn't care
about the insults, having long since become indifferent to
what other people think of her. She and her trolley, which is
filled with boxes of differing shapes and sizes and hung with
ancient plastic bags emblazoned with the logos of all the main
supermarkets, trundle down the canal path just as the first few
drops of rain fall on the town.

Molly doesn't speed up or take shelter under the trees that
line the canal path. Neither does she adjust her clothing or pull
her woolly hat lower down over her head. She is as indifferent
to the weather as she is to the opinions of others. Rain or shine,
it makes no odds to Molly, though when the winter snow is at
its deepest and sleeping under the bridge is impossible, she will
take herself off to the Homeless Shelter in the centre of town.

Molly doesn't mind it there, though they won't let her keep
her trolley by her bed because it is a fire hazard. She has to leave

it out in the small backyard, though they DO let her keep a few of her more important plastic bags with her.

They're not too bad at the Shelter, Molly thinks, for a bunch of do-gooders. They still haven't given up trying to get Molly to apply for council housing, though now they bring it up less frequently and with much less zeal. Molly meets their well-meaning, enthusiastic suggestions and enquiries with an unwavering indifference against which they have little defence.

The rain is falling heavily now as Molly turns off the canal path and onto Saint Cecilia's Avenue, at the top of which there is a small corner shop.

'Hallo there, Molly!' calls out the woman who owns the shop cheerfully as Molly and her trolley clatter in, dripping raindrops all over the shop floor. Molly rolls her eyes, though the woman, Ciara she is called, is nice enough and very well meaning, like the people at the shelter.

'Terrible weather we're having,' adds Ciara chattily from behind the counter, where she has been pricing tins of beans with her pricing gun. 'You wouldn't think it was summer at all, would you? Mind you, that's Irish weather for you,' she continues as Molly, who does not 'do' polite chitchat, grunts and parks her trolley next to the counter.

'I've kept aside a bottle of that gin you normally get and, as you can see, we've got a special offer on those biscuits you like, they're two for the price of one today', says Ciara as Molly shuffles round the small shop, throwing a few items into a basket – toilet paper, bars of chocolate, bananas, bread, chewing gum, a bottle of cola drink. Molly loves the sweet sugary taste and the biscuits on special offer.

'Thanks,' mutters Molly in response to the shop owner's chatter. The other woman's bright incessant babble irritates Molly, though deep down Molly knows she is probably being unfair to the woman who, after all, is only trying to be a decent human being.

'You haven't charged me for the biscuits,' says Molly now as the shop owner rings up the items at the till.

'Oh, have I not?' chirps Ciara, blushing furiously at having had her little act of kindness exposed. 'I'm sorry, my mistake,' she babbles, giving Molly the correct change. 'But they're on special offer today as you know so you're still only paying for one packet.'

But Molly is already hanging the plastic shopping bag for which she has not been charged onto her trolley which she manoeuvres awkwardly towards the door.

'Let me get that for you,' says Ciara, hurrying out from behind the counter to open the door.

'See you again,' she adds brightly as Molly and her trolley disappear through the shop door and out into the belting rain.

Molly merely grunts in reply. Ciara does not mind this too much. Some days Molly leaves the shop without acknowledging Ciara at all so, in the scheme of things, a grunt is an improvement. Ciara stands in the open shop doorway until Molly and her trolley have disappeared from sight.

Molly trundles back down the canal path the way she has come. She has opened her new packet of chewing gum and her jaws work rhythmically up and down. Molly likes the repetitive nature of the act of chewing gum. She finds it restful. She thinks, briefly, of the woman in the shop. She does not find Ciara restful.

Molly feels a prickling of guilt for having squashed the kindly shop owner's charitable impulses, but she, Molly, neither wants nor needs charity and she'd have thought the other woman would have gotten that into her head by now. Funny how there is always a 'sale' in the shop whenever Molly comes in, or an explosion of special offers.

When Molly arrives back at the bridge, the others are already there, sitting together on the damp grass, sheltering from the downpour. There is Freddie the alcoholic, who always cries out: 'Honey, I'm home!' when he arrives back at the bridge after a day's begging; Maura the alcoholic who has had the humour battered out of her over the years by life and the husband she tried many times to leave; Alan the drug addict, younger by far than the others in their strange little community of down-and-

185

outs, younger and somehow all the more tragic for his youth, and the waste of it.

Molly carefully parks her trolley and settles herself and her plastic bag of shopping down beside Maura, who is having one of her better days and actually grins and says 'Ta!' when Molly offers her a drink of gin.

Freddie and Alan are conducting an incoherent conversation of the kind Molly has heard them conduct many times before. She tunes out and takes a swallow of gin herself. Molly is not an alcoholic, but she is well aware of the powers of alcohol to take the edge off the day like today. Her leg is sore and she has a pain in her stomach which she doesn't think is caused by hunger. After a while she falls asleep and her head, still in its grey woolly hat, droops onto Maura's damp fleece covered shoulder.

A year passes and summer is here once more. Ciara is standing behind the counter of the little shop at the top of Saint Cecilia's Avenue chatting to one of her regulars. As she hands the man his change, out of the blue the man says: 'I've been meaning to ask you, whatever happed to old Molly, the trolley-lady? You know, the one who wore the grey woolly hat and had all the plastic bags hanging out of her trolley?'

Ciara hesitates before replying quietly, 'She didn't survive the winter.'

'You're joking!' says the man, though he can see that Ciara is not. He is a nice man and seems genuinely shocked.

'Was it hypothermia,' he asks. His tone is gentle as he can see that Ciara looks upset. Ciara nods.

'Among other things,' she replies. 'She had a tumour in her leg as well.'

'I'm very sorry to hear that,' says the man and Ciara can tell he is sincere. 'Many's the time I saw and heard old Molly trundling up the canal with that trolley of hers,' he continues. 'It was a crying shame she had to sleep rough, a woman of her age.'

'I think it was her own choice,' says Ciara quietly. 'She was a woman with a lot of problems.

'What was her story,' asks the man with interest. He is guessing, as many would, that a local shopkeeper might have the inside track.

'Well,' says Ciara, taking a deep breath, 'She was a very respectable, well-to-do lady once, a long time ago. She had a husband and a family and a nice house in a good area. But it all went wrong.'

'What happened,' asks the man.

'Her husband and son died in an accident,' continues Ciara. Her eyes are suspiciously bright. 'Molly was crazed with grief. She sold the family home and took to the streets. She vowed never to live in a house again. Never again to have anything she could lose. She had money from the sale of the house, but she never lived in a house again.'

'That's terrible,' replies the man, shaking his head as if in disbelief. He seems genuinely affected by Molly's story. 'Wasn't there - didn't she have anyone who could help her at all?'

'She had another child, a married daughter,' answers Ciara carefully. 'The daughter wanted to take her in, but Molly refused. She'd made up her mind to go on the streets and that's what she did.'

There is a silence as they each reflect on Molly's terrible decision. When her customer leaves, Ciara takes out from beneath the counter a framed photograph of herself, her dad, her brother and Molly in happier times, before the accident, before Molly took to the streets. Ciara knows that she is privileged that her mother, who could have lived anywhere, chose to set up camp down the road from her daughter's shop. She knows that this was Molly's way of maintaining contact with her daughter, her last link to her family, though at Molly's insistence their relationship was strictly confined to that of shopkeeper and customer, Molly's one stipulation, almost a deal breaker.

The bell above the shop door rings and a woman comes into the shop with two small children. Automatically Ciara begins to replace the photograph in its customary hiding place under the counter. It had remained hidden while Molly was a customer, for Molly could not have borne to see it and it has remained hidden, out of habit, since Molly's death.

At the sight of her mother's happy face smiling out of the photograph at her, Ciara changes her mind. She places the photograph on top of the counter where it will stay from now on, where everyone who comes in can see it. Then she turns to her customer and says in her brightest tones: 'What can I get you?'

The People Who Passed
Our Gate

A Memory By Sheelagh Mooney
Naas, Co. Kildare

The handsome white gates to the house offered a window on an exciting world to a curious three-year-old.

The gates into our house stood in impressive contrast to the small farmhouse that lay inside. They were huge, handsome, white iron gates that had been handmade for a more stately home than ours, but the purchaser decided he didn't want them after all and my Dad bought them. His intent had more to do with incarcerating errant cattle than providing a splendid frontage to our modest house.

The gates, all six feet of them, stood like an impassive policeman between me and freedom beyond. It was pointless to attempt to open them quietly, as the squeal would alert my mother to a potential escapee. So, I had to resort to sticking my head between the iron spikes and ornate squiggles in order the see into the waiting world beyond. In the evening I would take to my perch as the neighbours began to return from work.

The sound of a rattling bike heralded old Jim on his way back home after a day's work. In fact, Jim was probably not much more than fifty, but, to a three-year-old, he appeared very old. Despite his own big dependent family, Jim never failed to stop for a chat, followed by a lemon puff biscuit, which he would pull from a big bag in his pocket.

A low, distant rumbling, followed by a growing growl, meant that Tommy, who had recently graduated from a bike to a dark green Beetle, was on his way. He would toot his horn importantly, to great acclaim from me, as he sped past.

On other days, a middle-aged couple would pass on their bikes. The lady would always dismount and come over to the gate to enquire as to the health and welfare of my dolls and we would have lengthy discussions about the sort of frolics they would get up to when you weren't looking.

Her partner, a big tall man, would stand waiting patiently one foot on the pedal and one foot on the ground. He never got involved in these conversations, but since I never credited him with any knowledge of the world and foibles of dolls, I never attempted to involve him. Years later, I discovered that the pair was Frances Stuart, the writer, and his wife, Madeleine, who for some years lived in a little cottage a couple of miles from home.

Even then, there were the road hogs we were warned about and ours took the form of the fish man who drove a battered van at breakneck speed, the rising dust from which would have us scuttling back into the safety of the yard. On one occasion, he killed our young pup that had barely made his dash through the hedge to a short-lived freedom on the road. It was a harsh but valuable lesson for a young child on the dangers of road traffic.

The rear of our house was bounded by a river, which flowed under the road. Sometimes the road offered no diversion, but the river always did. Long days were spent in the company of my brother in the pursuit of the elusive big fish.

Every summer morning we would head for the river, armed with several jam jars and our new fishing rods – bamboo poles with little nets attached to the end. We would set up camp just close to the bridge and wait for the unsuspecting pinkeens coming down the river. When mealtimes came, my Mother would ring a little brass bell to alert everyone to come. This was essential since the times changed every day in accordance with my Mother's humour. You never quite knew whether to expect dinner or lunch, but the food was plentiful and tasty when it arrived and we had no complaint.

After meals, we would quickly retire again to the river and get on with the job in hand - to find the biggest pinkeen and bring him home in a large jam jar to sit over night in the kitchen window. My Mother tried to explain that we really shouldn't be taking the small fish from the river and even offered to buy us a goldfish. We laughed at the very idea of a pampered over-fed goldfish from a pet shop when we could fish for our own. We would take him back the following day and the whole procedure would begin again. We were hunter-gatherers and not ones to be messed with.

Life was simple and carefree in those days before the world outside came crashing in on our lives and took us beyond the protection of those big white gates, or that's how I remember it anyway.